SI Units

A Source Book

SI Units
A Source Book

G. S. RAMASWAMY
DIRECTOR
STRUCTURAL ENGINEERING RESEARCH CENTRE
ROORKEE, INDIA

&

V. V. L. RAO *(Deceased)*
LATE PRINCIPAL
REGIONAL ENGINEERING COLLEGE
WARANGAL, INDIA

TATA McGRAW-HILL PUBLISHING COMPANY LIMITED
BOMBAY   —   NEW DELHI

Published by Tata McGraw-Hill Publishing Company Limited, New Delhi
Printed in India at Indraprastha Press, New Delhi

TO

THE LATE PROFESSOR V.V.L. RAO

MY FRIEND AND COAUTHOR WHOSE DEVOTED

EFFORTS MADE THIS WORK POSSIBLE

Contents

Preface

In 1960, the General Conference on Weights and Measures recommended that SI (Systeme International d'Unites) should replace all other metric systems now in use. In 1962, both the International Organization for Standardization (ISO) and the International Electrotechnical Commission (IEC) endorsed the recommendation, thus setting the stage for a systematic change-over. Nearly thirty countries are committed to 'go SI' in the near future. Compulsions of world trade led the Federation of British Industries to recommend that the time-honoured Imperial system of weights and measures be dropped in favour of the metric system. As a result, Britian is now firmly committed to 'go metric' by the end of 1975. The British have wisely chosen to adopt SI, the latest version of the metric system. Australia and New Zealand are following in Britain's footsteps.

About 85 per cent of the world's population is already using the metric system in one form or another. About 75 per cent of world trade is being transacted in it. Hence, SI bids fair to become *the only metric system* used all over the world. It will very soon be the common currency or Scientific Esperanto among all the peoples of the world and in all fields of science, technology and engineering. Present expectations are that—barring the USA and Canada—all countries will adopt SI by 1975. Even in the USA and Canada, the benefits of 'going SI' are being carefully weighed and examined. Considerations of export trade will oblige them to fall in line with current world trends sooner or later.

Fortunately, we in India have already adopted the metric system by an Act of Parliament (Act 89 of 1956). It is understood that a suitable amendment to this Act is now on the anvil so that SI, the latest version of the metric system, becomes the only legally accepted system of weights and measures in India.

SI has a distinct edge over other versions of the metric system now in vogue. Stated briefly, its advantages are that it is *comprehensive, coherent* and *rational*. It is *comprehensive* in the sense that its six base units cover all disciplines. With the addition of the mole as the seventh base unit (this proposal is now under active consideration), there is hardly any discipline that SI will leave uncovered. The *coherence* of the system offers the advantage that the product or quotient of two or more of its units is the unit of the resultant quantity. It is *rational* because it has absorbed in itself the rationalized *RmksA* system pioneered by Giorgi for use in the electrotechnical sciences.

A language gulf now separates engineers, scientists and technologists. While the scientist uses absolute units, the engineer uses gravitational units and the technologist uses both. According to Professor M. J. Lighthill, F.R.S., a distinguished British authority on 'metrication' SI, an absolute system would bridge this gulf and provide a common language in which they can communicate with each other.

These advantages apart, SI promises to ease the burden on the very young in learning mathematics and science. According to Dr. E. G. Tagg, a British authority on methods of teaching mathematics, the total saving on account of adopting SI in teaching arithmetic at the primary level in the UK is expected to be £ 100 million per annum.

We need hardly labour the case for India 'going SI' at greater length in this brief preface.

The change-over to SI calls for careful and systematic spade-work. Among the steps involved is the introduction of SI at the school and college levels in teaching science and engineering for which SI-based textbooks are an urgent prerequisite. Our codes of practice will need to be rewritten as a preliminary to the introduction of SI in engineering practice. We can do no better than take a leaf from Britian where these preliminary steps have been very efficiently planned and executed. This book is written with the hope that it will, by providing information on SI, stimulate efforts in these directions in India.

Some good work has already been done by a number of organizations to prepare the ground for the change-over to SI. The Indian Standards Institution (ISI) which belongs to the ISO has already prepared a *Guide to the Use of International System (SI) of Units*. The Sub-committee on Education of the Indian National Science Academy under the chairmanship of Professor T. R. Seshadri, FRS, has already taken the initiative in bringing out five booklets to assist teachers at all levels in introducing SI. The Indian Institute of Technology, Madras, took the lead in organizing the first Refresher Course on SI units in December 1969 to familiarize teachers in technological institutions with the new system. My coauthor, the late Professor V.V.L. Rao, was in the forefront of these activities. His sudden passing away, when the book was under way, has been a grievous personal loss to me. He had patiently collected the material for this book from many sources which I am unable to completely identify. He had freely drawn on many good publications already available on SI and it is wellnigh impossible for me adequately to acknowledge our debt to various authors and publications. I can only beg of those concerned to forgive us for our trespasses as they are entirely unintentional. Adequate acknowledgements will be made in the second impression of the book, if my attention is drawn to such instances.

The author wishes to record his gratitude to Mr. M. N. Siddhanty and Mr. P. Senkaran, of the Indian Institute of Technology, for assisting him in working out a few examples.

G.S. RAMASWAMY

CHAPTER ONE

Units and Standards

1.1 Introduction

The ruins of Sumeria and Egypt bear witness to the existence of highly developed standards of mass and length as early as 300 BC. Measurement had its origins in trade and elementary civil engineering. The earliest demands in primitive societies were for weights and measures for barter of goods

Physical sciences and engineering involve precise measurements. Basically, measurements are a means of communication. They enable society to transact business at a techno-economic level. While the scientist uses measurements to understand natural phenomena, the engineer uses them for practical ends.

1.2 Measurement in Engineering and Science

Engineering is defined as knowledge applied to change our environmnent. There are three aspects of engineering:

(i) *Design:* planning of what has to be constructed
(ii) *Construction:* building what has been designed
(iii) *Organization:* arranging the cooperation of individuals required to execute the construction or design.

These three aspects are interdependent.

In all advanced engineering, *design* has to be carried out *numerically,* and this implies that measurements of comparable precision should be possible. The designer expresses his results in numerical terms. It is in this form that he communicates his instructions to the builder. Standards of measurement used by the builder must be the same as those used by the designer and this is most important when parts are made by different builders from different parts of the world.

Inherent in the idea of a standard is the concept that it is the same for everyone using it so that, in trade, it is the legal measure in which goods are bought and sold. In engineering, it enables a machine or structure designed in one place to be built at another. In science, it makes it possible to compare results obtained in one laboratory with those arrived at in another situated far away.

Criticism is essential for the progress of science; scientists can discuss and criticize the work of others only if they use the same measures and symbols. In measurement, this means that they must use the same units, symbols and standards; and the development of knowledge is dependent on international agreement on these matters.

1.3 Measurements, Units and Standards

Measurement is essentially counting, and counting is a process in arithmetic. Take the simplest example of measuring the value of a length, such as 25.40 mm, and stating the result thus:

Length=25.40 millimetres

In this, 'length' is the *quality* or name of the physical variable; 25.40 is the *precision* of the measurement indicated by the number of significant figures. Millimetres is the *unit* (mm), a statement in words or symbols of the basic standard of measurement. (In fact, we have freedom to use a variety of units: inches, feet, yards, centimetres, decimetres, metres, etc.) If we consider only the actual measuring process conducted in obtaining the above result, we find that we can write this as:

Length=25.40 x 1 mm

This description informs us that the unknown length has been compared with a standard of 1 mm in length and found to be 25.4 times as long as the standard.

Thus, *the measurement of length* reduces itself to *counting* the number of times that some standard interval can be placed end-to-end in the length that is to be measured, whether one does this operation with material bases or by counting the number of waves of interference maxima in an optical system in modern sophisticated quantum metrology.

The measurement of time, at its crudest, is nothing more than counting the number of times the sun traverses the sky from east to west or the number of times the seasons recur and, in its most refined forms, it is counting the number of oscillations of a radio-frequency signal that is producing atomic transitions.

All measurements however complex they may be, involve two operations:

(i) selection of a standard or unit amount of the *quantity* to be measured; and

(*ii*) counting the number of times the 'standard' is contained in the quantity to be measured.

Measurement, as we have seen above, can be best defined as the comparison of the magnitude of the entity to be measured with that of a similar entity whose magnitude is considered as the 'unit'. It is important that a clear distinction be drawn between the terms *units* and *standards*. These two terms will now be defined.

A *unit* is a value, quantity or magnitude in terms of which other values, quantities or magnitudes are expressed. Generally, a unit is fixed by definition and is independent of physical characteristics such as temperature. Examples of units are the metre, the litre and the kilogram.

A *standard* is a physical embodiment of a unit. It is often described by the French word *étalon*. In general, it is not independent of physical conditions. It is a true embodiment of the unit only under specified conditions, e.g. the standard metre has a length of one metre between the lines engraved on a platinum-iridium alloy bar of some definite composition at some definite temperature and when manufactured and supported in a certain manner. If supported in a different manner, it may have to be at a different temperature in order to have a length of one metre.

Measurement implies an extended use of number (as a result of counting) with the definite purpose of expressing the magnitude of a thing or a group. Arithmetically, it is the application of numbers for determining the properties of objects, phenomena and the like.

The essence of measurement is *comparison*. It is a process of comparing 'like things', making use of a 'standard' with which the thing or things can be compared. There are the 'natural units', as used by ancient man, mainly parts of the human body—span, palm, finger, cubit, foot, pace, grain (of corn), stone, cup, spoon etc.

Though these natural units serve the purpose of comparison or description, they are neither accurate nor uniform. Hence, the need to introduce standard measuring devices. Even in the barter of goods, the need was felt for uniform standards for *size* and *quality* and for subdivision into smaller units.

1.4 Standards in terms of Atomic Properties

Science and engineering require standards which are *well defined* and *convenient* so that

(*i*) there is *no doubt*, within the requisite accuracy, of what these standards are; and
(*ii*) everyone can speak the same numerical language.

The traditional standards are inadequate on both counts. Our standards of weight and mass are still arbitrary pieces of platinum or platinum-iridium. The 'pound standard' or 'kilogram standard' and similarly the standards of length were unitil recently *arbitrary,* being either a distance marked on a piece of metal or the distance between plane, parallel surfaces. These standards are *unique;* they cannot be reproduced in other laboratories by a recipe. Because of this, copies must be prepared and distributed to those who wish to use them and elaborate precautions need to be taken closely to guard the original against theft, damage or destruction. Such a system of standards is certainly not convenient. It is for these reasons that many measurements are now based on atomic phenomena and in a number of laboratories scientists are working towards replacing existing standards by ones based on atomic properties. This new science is called *quantum metrology.* The use of wave-lengths as standard for length measurements and of optical interference for making the measurements—first shown to be practical by Michelson more than half a century ago—are now widely known. On 14 October 1960, the Eleventh International Conference on Weights and Measures, meeting at Paris, redefined the metre as 1 650 763.73 wave-lengths of the orange-red spectrum line of the isotope of krypton having a mass number of 86. Nowadays, anyone who wishes to make measurements of length with high precision can set up an interforemeter and either a krypton-86 source or some other source giving a wave-length which bears a known relationship to that of the standard line (including stabilized gas lasers) and make his own measurements without any reference to a national laboratory such as the National Physical Laboratory.

In 1967, it was agreed internationally that the standard of time or frequency is to be the frequency of a certain atomic transition in the r.f. spectrum of caesium-133. Very precise radio and audio frequency standards as well as accurate time intervals can today be broadcast by National Standardization Laboratories and anyone with a simple radio receiver capable of being tuned to one of the frequencies transmitted can have access to them.

Atomic standards of length and frequency have thus become readily available in good laboratories. Electrical instrument manufacturers can check their frequency standards against broadcasts and precision mechanical engineering factories have their own optical interferometers for checking tool-makers' gauges. Atomic standards, besides beeing very convenient, are extremely precise. Two lamps giving nominally the same wave-length from krypton-86 agree to 1 part in 10^9. Standards of frequency similarly agree to about 1 part in 10^{12}.

Inaccuracies involved in astronomical observations are such that, in order to achieve an accuracy of 1 part in 10^{12}, the motion of the earth about the sun would have to be observed for about 100 million years. Moreover, the rotation of the earth about its axis varies by about about 1 part in 10^8. For these reasons, atomic standards have been adopted.

A certain number of independent standards is required in each branch of science. In geometry, we require a standard of length. To describe phenomena in mechanics, we must add standards of mass and time. In electro-dynamics, we require, in addition, a convenient electrical quantity. Conventionally, independent units of the intensity of light and temperature are also defined, but they are not essential. Intensity of light can be expressed in terms of mechanical units of energy. The concept of temperature is essentially a statistical property not unrelated to the concept of energy. However, it does, as a matter of convenience, help to include an arbitrary value like the temperature of the triple point of water to fix the magnitude of the temperature scale.

By using modern physical ideas, it is possible to reduce all these independent systems to a set depending on one arbitrary standard, viz. that of frequency. The relation of length to frequency is obvious, because if we use light waves for the measurement of length, then the frequency of the light itself enables us to determine a length if we know the velocity of light. In principle, we do not need an independent standard of length, but an arbitrary element remains in our definition of length because we adopt for the velocity of light the arbitrary value which has been found by comparison with the arbitrary standards of frequency and length. If everyone agrees internationally on the value of the speed of light to be adopted, it should be possible *in principle* for anyone measuring lengths by optical interference to determine his standard by tuning in to a standard radio frequency broadcast. The adopted value for the speed of light can, in principle, be quite arbitrary; but it is very desirable that it should be such that measurements of length derived from frequency through the adopted value should be equivalent to those made in terms of the existing krypton standard. Before a conventional value of the speed of light can be adopted internationally, it is desirable to measure the speed in terms of the present standards of length and frequency to the highest possible degree of accuracy.

1.5 Basic Standards

In mechanics, measurements involve three units:

(*i*) a unit of length,
(*ii*) a unit of mass, and
(*iii*) a unit of time.

It has been realized from very ancient times that certain considerations need to be kept in view in selecting suitable standards. These are:

(*i*) it must be possible to define them unambiguously,
(*ii*) they must be easy to copy,
(*iii*) they must be invariable with time and place, i.e. immutable, and
(*iv*) methods must be available for multiplying or subdividing each one of the standards.

If these criteria are satisfied, then the size of the unit may be arbitrarily selected. We have already seen that the essence of all physical measurements is comparison with standards. The ultimate purpose in refining experimental techniques is to facilitate or enhance accuracy in making these comparisons. The latest definitions for length and time units are atomic definitions. The reproducibility of the atomic definition of the length unit is 1 part in 10^8 and that of the time unit is 1 part in 10^{11}. No apropriate atomic definition has been possible for mass. It has not yet been possible to excel the reproducibility of about 1 part in 10^8 attributed to the International Kilogram and its authorized copies.

1.6 Metric and SI Systems

The idea of a decimal system of units was first proposed by Simon Stevin (1548-1620). He also developed the concept of decimal fractions. The credit for devising a decimal-based measuring system is usually given to G. Mouton, a priest from Lyon in France who proposed it in 1670. Decimal units were also considered in the early days of the French Academie des Sciences founded in 1666; but the adoption of the metric system as a practical measure was a part of the general increase in administrative activity in Europe following the French Revolution. Thus, 'the metric system' based on the metre as the unit of length, originated in France in the wake of the French Revolution. Under the orders of the statesman Talleyrand, the French scientists of the day, Lagrange and Laplace among them, developed a new international decimal system of weights and measures for adoption by all in place of the then current feudalistic standards and units. To make this new system both universal and unvarying, it was decided to formulate a decimal-based system and to adopt from nature a definite and invariable unit. At the suggestion of the French scientist Picard and the Dutch savant Huygens, the length of a seconds pendulum at sea level and at a latitude 45° was designated as the 'metre' and the multiples and sub-divisions of the metre on the decimal system were also established. The following terms denote the order and sequence in the system:

Kilometre	=	10 hectometres
	=	100 decametres
	=	1000 metres
Metre	=	10 decimetres
	=	100 centimetres
	=	1000 millimetres

Unfortunately, the length of the pendulum was not generally accepted as an accurate conventional length. The physicist Borda, the mathematician Lagrange, and the chemist Lavoisier suggested a new definition for the 'metre' in 1791. According to the new definition, a 'metre' was defined as $1/10^7$ of the quadrant of the great circle of the earth passing through Paris and the North and South Poles. The original standard metre bar known as the *metre des archives* was made of platinum in 1793. Its length at 0°C was supposedly $1/10^7$ of the earth's meridian quadrant at sea level. The word metre occurs for the first time in 1793 in one of the reports of the French National Academy. Two French engineers, Delambre and Mechain, were entrusted with the work of measuring a portion of this meridian—a circle passing through the North and South Poles. This portion was the arc connecting Dunkirk in France with Barcelona in Spain at sea level and 45° latitude. The then prevailing circumstances did not permit this aim to be achieved with the desired accuracy. The task of measuring accurately the distance between Dunkirk and Barcelona during the height of the Revolution was completed by 1798 and the results of the survey were checked by several committees. On 22 June 1798, a platinum-iridium line standard was finally adopted as the standard measure of the 'metre'. The metre was defined as the distance between two lines on the bar at 0°C. The word 'metre' is derived from the Greek word *metron* and the latin word *metrum* (=to measure). This is the history of the birth of the metre and consequently of the 'metric system' of which SI is the latest version.

The work of establishing a standard weight based on the mass of one cubic centimetre of water was undertaken by Lavoisier, the chemist. The gramme was accordingly chosen as the unit quantity of matter. It was defined as the mass of one cubic centimetre of water at 0°C.

It was prescribed that the relationship between the units of *mass,* volume, and length should be direct and specific. The capacity of a cube 1/10 metre side was designated a 'litre', the standard unit of capacity or volume. The accurate weight of water contained in the cube came to be known as the 'kilogram', the standard unit of mass. The prototype 'kilogram' was a platinum cylinder whose diameter and height were both equal to 39 millimetres.

The metric system outlined above was adopted by the French Assembly in 1799. It became the sole legal system only in 1840. During this period of forty years, many other countries and states recognized or adopted the metric system. Thus arose the need for international coordination. In 1870, the French Government called an international conference attended by delegates from 30 countries. Though the conference was interrupted by the Franco-Prussian war, it met again in 1872 and 1875. On the completion of the conference, the *convention du metre* (the Metre Convention) was signed in 1875. This convention brought into existence the Bureau of Weights and Measures at Sevres, near Paris. Its first work was to prepare the international prototype of the metre and the kilogram. Thus, France has been using the metric system for more than 130 years. Many other nations have also adopted it. It is universally used by scientists in the form of the cgs system. Even though the metric system was essentially devised to directly benefit industry and commerce, physicists and chemists soon realized its advantages in the laboratory and it was generally adopted in scientific and technical circles as a result of the selection by the British Association for the Advancement of Science of the centimetre and the gramme as the basic units of length and mass for physical purposes. Adoption of the second as the basic unit of time led to the centimetre-gramme-second (cgs) system so well-known in all science laboratories of the world since 1873.

Unfortunately, the fundamental quantities of the cgs system were too inconveniently small for the work-a-day world and, therefore, not suitable for engineering, technology and commerce. As electrical science developed in the 20th century, some serious defects were noticed in the scientific cgs system. It was to overcome these difficulties that Giovami Giorgi, a professor of Electrical Engineering at the University of Rome, proposed the mks or metre-kilogram-me-second system. It was formally adopted in 1935 by the International Electrotechnical-Commission (IEC) at its Scheviningen (Holland) meeting. In 1946, it was accepted as the mksA

system, making the ampere the fourth fundamental unit drawn from the field of electricity and magnetism after consideration for nearly half a century. Finally, in 1954, at the 10th Conference Generale des Poids et Mesures (General Conference of Weights and Measures —CGPM), the 'rationalized' RmksA system was adopted. Though the name SI was formally used to describe the system only in 1960, we may say that the birth of SI dates back to 1954. France has made SI the legal system of weights and measures. It is gaining ground in a number of countries. It is hoped that ultimately SI will be the *only* metric system in use in all parts of the world.

In all fairness, it needs to be mentioned that SI does not represent the ultimate in the evolution of a physical system. It is the best available now, in 1971, suitable for all disciplines such as mechanics, thermodynamics and electro-technology. It is a unified coherent system with six base units, two supplementary units and a large number of derived units to cover the needs of all disciplines. The SI system is described in Chapter 2.

To sum up, there have been at least three different forms of the metric system—(*i*) cgs, (*ii*) mks, (*iii*) RmksA— before SI (with six base units) was evolved.

It is the object of this book to provide data on SI units and to encourage strict adherence to 'coherent' units (defined later) of the SI as far as possible. This involves the discarding of several historically established derived units such as the calorie and horse-power which are not based on SI units and also of other unit-combinations which though 'metric' are not 'coherent'. The main reason for the universal and ready adoption of SI is that it is incomparably simpler than all the previous metric systems and the fps (Imperial) system.

CHAPTER TWO

Introduction to SI Units

2.1 Origin of the SI System

SI is the abbreviation by which the Système International d' Unités (International System of Units) is now known in any language.

It is, as mentioned in Chapter 1, the latest form of the metric system and differs in points of detail from the three earlier versions, viz. the cgs, the mks and RkmsA, systems.

The 'internationalism' of the metric units is one of the main advantages claimed for the metric language of measurement. The second advantage is that it serves as a link and common language between scientist and engineer. Hence, its benefits cannot be realized to the fullest extent unless we adopt a version of the metric system which is both understood and used by most scientists and engineers in all countries of the world.

The Conference Generale des Poids et Mesures (CGPM) provides an international forum for all engineers and scientists concerned with metric measurement. It is the authority set up by the Metric Convention of 1875 *'to promote the use and effect improvements in the metric system and to secure international uniformity in metric units and standards of measurement'*. It consists of delegations from about forty member nations which meet usually once in six years or more

often, if necessary. The 10th, 11th, 12th and 13th conferences were held in 1954, 1960, 1964 and 1967. The Bureau Internationl des Poids et Mesures (The International Bureau for Weights and Measures)—usually abbreviated BIPM—situated at Sevres in France, is the central office and laboratory of the organization which is managed, under the authority of the General Conference, by the International Committee of Weights and Measures (Comité International des Poids et Mesures, abbreviated as CIPM) consisting of 18 members from different nations. This international committee meets every year and has the responsibility for recommending proposals for approval by the CGPM. Seven special advisory committees assist the international committee on planning cooperative programmes of research and the preparation of recommendations or units of measurement, viz. length (definition of the metre), time (definition of the second), temperature, electricity, photometry and ionizing radiation.

In 1960, the CGPM recommended that SI should replace the existing metric system. In 1962, both the International Standards Organization (ISO) and the International Electrotechnical Commission (IEC) endorsed the re-commendation.

Recommendations on world standards are made by the ISO. Even though the ISO has no legal powers in any country, its recommendations are agreements by a majority of the 50-odd countries (including India) which support it. The ISO is not connected directly with the maintenance of the metric physical standards (étalons), but has a close liaison with the BIPM which is charged with that duty. International recommendations on electrical matters are dealt with by the IEC, the electrical wing of the ISO. ISO and IEC publications are available in India from the Indian Standards Institution.

The International Organization for Legal Metrology (OIML) helps individual countries in preparing legislation to implement decisions of the CGPM. The decisions of the CGPM are incorporated into Indian Law through Acts of the Indian Parliament, mainly the Indian Weights and Measures Act, No. 89 of 1956, and its amendments in 1960 and 1964 (given in Appendix I). This Act recognizes the six base units of SI and a bill is now under preparation modifying the Act to recognize all the SI units.

About 90 per cent of the world's population at present uses the metric system in one form or other. Hence, the prospect of SI being universally adopted is now rather bright. Since the principal metric countries have already resolved to adopt SI in a matter of a few years, it will soon be the only system used throughout the world. Compulsions of world trade led British industry to opt for a straight change over to the SI system when Britain decided to go metric. So, by 1975, the only major industrial countries which would not have changed to the metric system may possibly be the USA and Canada. It is interesting, however, to note that in August 1968 the US Congress authorised the US National Bureau of Standards (NBS) to make a comprehensive study of the relative advantages and disadvantages involved in switching over to the SI system. Moreover,

TABLE 2.1

ADOPTION OF SI UNITS IN SELECTED COUNTRIES

Countries changing over to SI	Countries using the metric system	Countries changing over to the metric system
Australia	Argentina	Eire
Austria	China	Ghana
Brazil	Greece	Kenya
Czechoslovakia	India	Kuwait
East Germany	Israel	Pakistan
West Germany	Mexico	South Africa
Italy	Sweden	Tanzania
Japan	Turkey	Uganda
New Zealand		
UK		
USSR		

even now both the NBS and the US National Aeronautics and Space Administration (NASA) have been publishing data in SI units. As for Canada, a White Paper on its intention to go metric has just been published. The present position relating to metric units in certain countries is given in Table 2.1.

2.2 Base Units

SI is a *coherent* system. What this means is explained in Sec. 2.4. Irrespective of whether a system is coherent or not, unit values need to be assigned to arbitrarily selected magnitudes of certain physical quantities. These magnitudes form a set of standards. There is no coherent relationship between the value so defined of one magnitude and another of the same system. These arbitrarily selected magnitudes do not also bear any coherent relationship with their derived units. In a coherent system such as SI, the *arbitrarily* selected units are called basic or base units. Since the use of the term *basic units* may convey the impression that there is something absolute or basic about them, in what follows, to avoid confusion, the term *base units* will be used to designate these arbitrarily chosen magnitudes. Also, *base units* is the nearest equivalent to the French *unite de base*. SI employs six base units: the metre, the kilogram, the second, the ampere, the kelvin and the candela (Appendix II).

2.3 SI Base Units

SI is based on a rationalized selection of six of the present metric units. From these units all other physical quantities are derived coherently. The six base units are given in Table 2.2.

2.4 A Coherent System

A unit system is coherent if the product or quotient of two or more of its units is the unit of the resultant quantity. For example, in a coherent system

m^2, the unit area, results when a unit length (m) is multiplied by another unit length (m);

m^3, the unit volume results when the unit area (m^2) is multiplied by unit length (m^3);

m/s, unit velocity, results when the unit length (m) is divided by unit time (s); and

kg m/s^2 unit force results when the unit mass (kg) is multiplied by unit acceleration $m/(s)^2$.

NOTE: The coherent unit of velocity is the metre per second (m/s) and not kilometre per hour (km/h). As we have seen above, the coherent unit of force is that force which imparts to the unit mass (kg) an acceleration of one metre per second^2 (m/s^2). This unit of force is called the newton (symbol: $N = kg\ m/s^2$). This is the *most important unit* in SI because it occurs as a factor in many of the units which are commonly used in physical sciences such as pressure, stress, energy and power.

The main differences between the SI (an absolute metric system) and the metric-technical or engineer's system (a gravitational system) are summarised in Table 2.3.

Table 2.4 gives some derived units used in mechanics.

Table 2.5 gives SI derived units with special names.

TABLE 2.2

SI BASE UNITS

Physical quantity	SI unit	Abbreviation for SI unit
1. Length	metre	m
2. Mass	kilogram	kg
3. Time	second	s
4. Electric current	ampere	A
5. Luminous intensity	candela	cd
6. Thermodynamic temperature	kelvin*	K
7. Amount of substance	mole	mol (not yet officially recognized)

The two dimensionless supplementary units are:

1. Plane angle	radian	rad
2. Solid angle	steradian	sr

*Should be kelvin only and not degree kelvin or °K.

TABLE 2.3

SI AND METRIC-TECHNICAL UNITS

System	Mass unit	Absolute unit of force	Practical unit of force
FPS	pound	weight of one pound mass	poundal (pdl)
Metric technical	gram kilogram	gf kgf	dyne (dyn) kilopound(kp)
SI	kilogram	newton	

TABLE 2.4

DERIVED UNITS

Symbol	Physical quantity	Name of unit
m^2	area	square metre
m^3	volume	cubic metre
$kg\,m^{-3}$	density	kilogram per cubic metre
$m\,s^{-1}$	velocity	metre per second
$m\,s^{-2}$	acceleration	metre per second/second or metre per second^2
$rad\,s^{-1}$	angular velocity	radian/second^2
$rad\,s^{-2}$	angular acceleration	radian/second^2

TABLE 2.5

DERIVED SI UNITS

Physical quantity	Name of SI unit	SI unit symbol
Force	newton	$N = kg\,m/s^2$
Work, energy, quantity of heat	joule	$J = N\,m$
Power	watt	$W = J/s = N\,m/s$
Electric charge	coulomb	$C = A\,s$
Electric potential	volt	$V = W/A$
Electric capacitance	farad	$F = A\,s/V$
Electric resistance	ohm	$\Omega = V/A$
Inductance	henry	$H = V\,s/A$
Solid angle	steradian	sr
Luminous flux	lumen	$lm = cd\ sr$
Illumination	lux	$lx = lm/m$
Frequency	hertz	$Hz = s^{-1}$
Flux of magnetic induction, Magnetic flux	weber	$Wb = Vs$
Magnetic flux density, Magnetic induction	tesla	$T = Wb/m^2$
Customary temperature	degree celsius*	°C

*The Centigrade scale has been renamed the Celsius scale to fall in line with international practice. Moreover, in France, the term 'grade' is used for 1/100th of a right angle and so centigrade means 1/10 000 of a right angle.

2.5 Derived Units

Units that are a combination of two or more quantities and which usually require a compound word to name them are called *compound* or *derived* units, Thus, a square with each side 2 metres in length has area 2m $\times$ 2m = 4m^2 = 4 square metres (m^2 is read as 'square metres'). Often, the units of a physical quantity are hidden in a statement about a measurement. Thus, the magnitude of an angle can be given as the ratio of the length of the arc subtended by the angle to the radius of the arc, both having been measured in the same units. Because it is awkward to express an angle as 1, 2, 3 or 0.5 without mentioning the unit, we attach an artificial name, the *radian*, to these numbers. Really, this unit is not at all needed. It is introduced only for convenience. If a convenient standard already exists, then one can express a quantity in terms of this standard and thus in practice suppress the units, e.g. the density of water in SI is 1000 kg/m^3 and the density of turpentine is 870 kg/m^3. For the sake of convenience, we can define the *specific gravity* or *relative density* of a substance as the ratio of its density to that of water. So, the relative density of turpentine is 0.870 and it has no units, being a ratio. This method of sup-pressing units is common in both physics and engineering.

Appendix III gives the definitions of derived units.

2.6 Concept of Dimensions

The length of an object is a concept which is easily recognized and does not depend on how it is measured or on the units used to describe it. For example, measurements such as length = 5 miles, breadth = 3 metres, thickness = 2 $\times$ 10^{-5} mm or an astronomical distance of 3.260 light years—all have one characteristic in common: they are all 'lengths', even though the units used to express them may differ. Any physical quantity that can be measured in units of length is said to have the dimension of length. So, the concept of *dimension* is more generalized than the concept of *unit*. This dimension concept permits us to characterize all physical quantities as composed of a few 'basic' or base dimensions. Any physical quantity, however complex can be expressed in terms of these base dimensions.

If length, mass and time are considered as the base dimensions, we can specify the dimensions of velocity or speed as length/time or $L/T=[LT^{-1}]$. The dimensions of acceleration are velocity/time or L/T^{-2}. The dimensions of density=mass/volume=$[ML^{-3}]$. The dimensions of force=mass×acceleration=$[MLT^{-2}]$. The dimensions of pressure = force/area = $[ML^{-1}T^2]$. The dimensions of kinetic energy= (mass. velocity^2)=$[ML^2T^{-2}]$. The dimensions of power=(energy/time)=$[ML^2T^{-3}]$. The dimensions of momentum=(mass)(velocity)=$[MLT^{-1}]$ Radian measure has no dimensions because it is a *ratio* of length to length. In this way, we can derive the dimensional equation of any physical quantity which will hold good for any set of units. The 'dimensions' of a quantity are, in reality, a statement about its basic nature.

2.7 Supplementary Units

The SI unit for plane angles is the radian (rad); the SI unit for measuring solid angles is the steradian (sr). For angular measurements, there are two natural units:

(*i*) the radian, and
(*ii*) the revolution.

SI also recognizes for revolution or cycles a unit, long in vogue on the continent of Europe, the hertz (Hz). Frequency has the dimension T^{-1}. For calculations in trignometry, the radian is widely used; for example:

$\pi/2$ radians=$90°$; or π radians=$180°$

From this, 1 radian=$57.3°=57°$ 17′ 44″. Conversely, $1° = 1/180$ radian=0.017 rad.

The steradian, the solid angle unit, is defined as the solid angle subtended at the centre of a sphere by an area on the surface of the sphere which is numerically equal to the square of the radius. That is, number of steradians=(area/radius^2). Since the area of the surface of a sphere is $4\pi r^2$, it at once follows that the total solid angle subtended by a point in all directions is 4π steradians written as 4πsr. However, steradian is used very rarely.

2.8 Some Rules and Conventions

USE AND SPACING OF SYMBOLS

(*i*) Full names of units, even when they are named after a person, are not written with a capital initial letter, e.g. kelvin, newton, joule, watt, volt, ampere etc.

(*ii*) The *symbol* for a unit, named after a person, has a capital initial letter, e.g. W for watt (after James Watt) and J for joule (after James Prescott Joule).

(*iii*) Symbols for other units are not written with capital letters, e.g. m for metre.

(*iv*) Units may be written out in full or using the agreed symbols, but no other abbreviations may be used. They are printed, in full or abbreviated, in roman (upright) type.
R S* 1969 states: 'The symbols for units specified are mandatory.'

(*v*) Symbols for units do not take a plural form with added 's'; the symbol merely names the unit in which the preceding magnitude is measired, e.g. 50 kg not 50 kgs, 4.2 J not 4.2 Js.

(*vi*) No full stops or other punctuation marks should be used with in or at the ends of symbols for units to indicate abbreviations or initials or even while writing SI, e.g. 3 m not 3 m., 'SI units' not 'S.I. units'.

*RS stands for the British Royal Society's publication: *Symbols, Signs and Abbreviations Recommended for British Scientific Publications* (London, 1969).

(vii) There is a mixture of capital and lower-case letters in the symbols for the prefixes, but the full names of the prefixes commence with lower case letters only, e.g. 5 MW (5 megawatts), 2 ns (2 nano-seconds)

(viii) A space is left between the numeral and the symbol except in the case of the permitted non-SI units for angular measurements, e.g. 57° 16′ 44″.

(ix) A similar space is left between the symbols for compound units, e.g. N m for newtons × metres and kW h for kilowatt hour. [This reduces the risk of confusion when an index notation, instead of the solidus (/) is used. In the former notation, a velocity in metres per second is written as ms^{-1} instead of m/s, but ms^{-1} may mean 'per millisecond'. However, a measurement involving this will not occur if the guidance rule given later is followed.

DIGITAL REPRESENTATION OF NUMERICAL VALUES

(i) *Numerals of more than three digits.* Such numerals should be written in groups of three with a narrow space between consecutive groups. The grouping should start from the unit digit and move towards the left when there is no decimal point. When there is a decimal point, the grouping should be done in both directions from the decimal point.

(ii) The use of a punctuation mark (e.g. a comma) for breaking up numerals should be avoided. It is recognized, however, that to drop the comma from commercial accounting will involve difficulties, particularly with the adding machines in use at present.

(iii) A sequence of four figures is not generally broken into groups, e.g. 1234.0036.

Digital representation of numerical values: Examples

	Incorrect		*Correct*
(1)	40,000 or 40000	(1)	40 000
(2)	81234.765	(2)	81 234.765
(3)	7 642 13.876	(3)	764 213.876
(4)	345 6.7	(4)	3456.7
(5)	0.123547	(5)	0.123 547

This rule states that denominators of compound units are always expressed in the base units and not in their multiples or sub multiples. Thus, a heat flow rate will not be given as J/m s but only as KJ/s=kW.]

(x) Algebraic symbols representing *quantities* are written in italics, while symbols for *units* are written in upright characters, e.g.

$$\text{a current } I = 3 \text{ A}$$
$$\text{an emf } E = 5 \text{ } \mu\text{v}$$

Exceptions

A numeral may also be written without short-spacing in the following cases:

(i) Designation of a standard specification, e.g. IS 3619 — 1966

(ii) date, e.g. 12 May 1970

(iii) hour of day, e.g. 1000 h

Decimal Marks in Engineering Drawings

As yet, there is no international recommendation on this. B.S. 308 on engineering drawings issued in 1964 gave the comma as the decimal marker for metric dimensions in line with Continental practice.

2.9 Size of Units: Multiples & Sub-multiples

The choice of the metre and the kilogram as base units of length and mass, compared to the centimetre and gram of the cgs system yields coherently derived units of more practical value in many cases. Even so, not all the coherent units are of a convenient size for all applications, especially in engineering and technology. The metre, for instance, is a convenient unit for building-site plans, but is too large for precision engineering purposes and too small for the expression of large distances between towns, let alone astronomical distances. Therefore, provision had to be made for multiples and sub-multiples of the coherent units. A complete list of such factors is given in Table 2.6.

TABLE 2.6

MULTIPLE AND SUB-MULTIPLE FACTORS

Multiplier	Prefix	Symbol	Origin	Original meaning	Example
10^{12}	tera*	T	Greek	Monstrous	terametre
10^9	giga†	G	Greek	gigantic	gigacycle
10^6	mega	M	Greek	great	megaton
13^3	kilo	k	Greek	thousand	kilometre
10^2	hecto	h	Greek	hundred	hectogram
10^1	deca	da	Greek	ten	decade
10^{-1}	deci	d	Latin	tenth	decimetre
10^{-2}	centi	c	Latin	hundredth	centimetre
10^{-3}	milli	m	Latin	thousandth	milligram
10^{-6}	micro	μ	Greek	small	microgram
10^{-9}	nano	n	Greek	very small	nanosecond
10^{-12}	pico	p	Spanish	extremely small	picofarad
10^{-15}	femto	f	Scandinavian	fifteen	fermi ($=10^{-15}$m)
10^{-18}	atto	a	Scandinavian	eighteen	acoulomb ($=10^{-18}$coulomb)

*Bold face has been used for prefixes most widely used.
†Pronounced *jeega*.

Notes :

1. All prefixes denoting magnitudes > 1 are of Greek origin.
2. Almost all abbreviations of prefixes for magnitudes < 1 are English lower-case letters. An exception is micro (Greek letter μ).
3. Abbreviations of prefixes for magnitudes > 1 are English upper-case letters. Exceptions are: kilo, hecto and deca.
4. Unfortunately, the prefixes deci- and deca- have a somewhat similar spelling and pronunciation.
5. Several US organizations like the Institute of Electrical & Electronic Engineers, New York, and the National Bureau of Standards, Washington, prefer the spelling deka for deca.
6. The prefixes hecto, deca, deci and centi should not be used unless there is a strongly felt need.

GUIDELINES RECOMMENDED FOR INTERNATIONAL
APPLICATION OF PREFIXES

1. Reduce the number of new names to be used for the prefixes. Multiples of the fundamental unit should be chosen in powers of $\pm 3n$, where n is an integer. Centimetre, owing to its well-established usage and its convenient size in the laboratory, cannot be given up lightly.
2. The prefixes for multiples and sub-multiples should be used only for SI units.
3. Double prefixes should be avoided, e.g. instead of millimicrometre, use nanometre (nm).
4. To simplify calculations attach the prefix to the numerator and not to the denominator, e.g. use MN/m^2 instead of N/mm^2, even though mathematically both forms are equivalent.
5. The rules for binding-in indices are not those of ordinary algebra: i.e.
   cm^2 means $(cm)^2 = (0.01)^2 \ m^2 = 0.0001 \ m^2$ and not $c \times (m)^2 = 0.01 \ m^2$.

2.10 Practical Application of SI Units

An ISO Committee has published a draft recommendation concerning the use of SI units and has, in general, observed two very important and practical principles:

(i) Any unit which is already internationally recognized and used shall not be lightly discarded even though the unit in question is a non-SI unit or a non-preferred multiple of an SI unit.
(ii) To facilitate international communication, the number of preferred multiples for any particular unit should be restricted, so that in any particular application the probability of all concerned using the same multiple or sub-multiple will be greater.

A preference has been expressed for multiples or sub-multiples involving the factor

$1000 (= 10^{\pm 3n})$. From the above two rules, the following important conclusions are drawn:

(i) The internationally accepted time units, namely, minute, hour, day, week, month and year, will continue to be used.
(ii) The division of the circle into 360 degrees and the sub-division of the degree, the minute and the second, will also continue for trignometrical purposes.
(iii) The supplementary SI unit, the radian, will, however, figure in problems of dynamics as at present.

FURTHER RULES PRESCRIBED

(i) The rule forbidding double-prefixes leads to an anomaly. The kg, the basic unit of mass in SI, is a multiple of the basic unit of the cgs system (the gram). Since double prefixes are not allowed, any multiple or sub-multiple of the kilogram must naturally be a different multiple or sub-multiple of the gram. Thus, 1000 kg or 1 metric ton or 1 tonne (t) will have to be written only as 1 Mg, while one millionth of the kilogram will be written as 1 mg.
(ii) If it is desired to modify the size of a unit which is a quotient, then the requisite prefix should be applied only to the numerator of the fraction, e.g. N/m^2, unit of pressure or stress, is very small. More convenient values are obtained by using kN/m^2 or MN/m^2 or GN/m^2, rather than N/cm^2.

The following examples show how tensile strength and the Young's Modulus of materials may be expressed:

Tensile strength for wrought iron: $2.9 \times 10^8 \ N/m^2$, E for wrought iron is $3 \times 10^{11} \ N/m^2$ or better still, $0.3 \times 10^{12} \ N/m^2$ (to conform to the $\pm 3n$ rule for indices and also to adjust the multiplying value to lie between the range 0.1 and 1000).

CHAPTER THREE

SI Units in Physics

3.1 Systems of Units Used in Mechanics

The science of mechanics deals with the description of material objects and their motion in space and time. It is a branch of physics directly connected with observable phenomena in daily life. If we describe the length, area, volume, density, mass, force, velocity or acceleration of a material object, we are using the terminology, concepts and units employed in mechanics. It Is an old science. Its laws are well-known and we can formulate the units of measurement for all the concepts involved in mechanics from a few base quantities. The base concepts which we choose are called the dimensions of the system. The corresponding set of units define a system of units. Three dimensions are enough to express all concepts in mechanics. Choosing concepts which are considered base concepts is purely arbitrary. There are two common systems in vogue:

(i) the length-mass-time set, i.e. dimensions: L, M and T.
(ii) the length-force-time set, i.e. dimensions: L, F and T.

Even with these two sets of dimensions, many different systems of units can be used. With L,

M and T dimensions, for instance, we could use the cm-gram-second (cgs) or the metre-kilogram-second (mks) system.

In the first system, force will be measured in cm grams sec^{-2} and in the second in metre kilogram sec^{-2}. These compound units are called the 'dyne' and the 'newton' respectively.

The process of constructing systems of dimensions involves the selection of various constants that appear in a physical equation, e.g. Newton's Second Law of Motion which may be written as $F = k.ma$, where m is the mass of a body, a is the acceleration and k is a constant of proportionality. Hence, we may write the following dimensional equation:

$$[F] = [M] \left[\frac{L}{T^2}\right] = [MLT^{-2}]$$

Units, in principle, as stated already, may be chosen arbitrarily, but making such an arbitrary choice of a unit for each set of mutually comparable quantities leads, in general, to the appearance of several additional numerical factors in the equations between the numerical values. A system of units in which the equations between numerical values, including the numerical factors, have exactly the same form as the corresponding equations between the quantities is termed *coherent* with respect to the system of quantities and equations in question. In a coherent unit system, equations between units contain a numerical factor of only unity, e.g. in Newton's Second Law of Motion, $F=k.ma$, $k=1$. This implies that, when the units of any two quantities are chosen independently, the unit of the third is automatically fixed. Thus, when we say that a system is coherent, we mean that the product or quotient of two or more of its units is the unit of the resultant quantity.

Let us first consider the most commonly used systems of units in mechanics.

In the cgs system, the basic dimensions are length, mass and time. It was first proposed in 1795 and adopted in France in 1799. Since then, it spread throughout the scientific world. It is very useful in physics and chemistry. The unit of length is 1 cm; the unit of mass is 1 gram and the unit of time is 1 second. Unfortunately, the cgs unit of force (absolute) is 1 dyne which is too small for most practical and technical (engineering) purposes. The dyne is defined as the force required to produce an acceleration of 1 cm/s² when acting on a mass of 1 gram. This is nearly one-millionth of a pound weight. In the mks system, the basic dimensions are again length, mass and time. This is the most widely used system in the world, both in science and engineering. In this system, the unit of length is 1 metre, the unit of mass 1 kg, the unit of time 1 second. The mks 'absolute' system is a part of SI. Table 3.1 gives the dimensions of important physical quantities incgs and mks or SI systems.

Among the Imperial or British systems of units in mechanics, the most important one is the fps gravitational system in which the basic dimensions are the foot, the pound force and the second. This is in common use in many English-speaking countries but is now being rapidly replaced by the cgs, mks or SI systems, because the fps (gravitational) is of limited use. Its main drawback is that it cannot be extended

TABLE 3.1

PHYSICAL QUANTITIES IN CGS AND SI UNITS

Physical quantity	Dimension	cgs unit	SI or mks (absolute unit)
Length	L	centimetre (cm)	metre (m)
mass	M	gram (g)	kilogram (kg)
time	T	second (s)	second (s)
velocity	$\dfrac{L}{T}$	cm/s	m/s
acceleration	$\dfrac{L}{T^2}$	cm/s²	m/s²
force	$\dfrac{ML}{T^2}$	dyne (cm. g/s²)	newton (kg.m/s²)
energy	$\dfrac{ML^2}{T^2}$	erg (g.cm²/s²)	joule (kg.m²/s²)
power	$\dfrac{ML^2}{T^3}$	(g.cm²/s³)	watt (kg.m²/s³)

to the field of electricity and magnetism. In a gravitational system such as the fps system, Newton's Second Law of motion may be written as:

$W = mg$, where W is the weight and g
  the acceleration due to gravity
$g = 32$ ft/s² in the fps system
  $= 981$ cm/s² in the cgs system
  $= 9.81$ m/s² in the mks or SI system

Correspondingly, in the mks (gravitational) system, the unit of force is a kilogram force (kgf). It is a non-coherent unit and is defined as that force which, when applied to a mass of one kilogram, produces in it an accleration of 9.806 65 m/s².

Thus, in a gravitational system, when we deal with masses moving under the influence of gravity, g does not appear in the equations, while, if the problem is in no way influenced by gravity a g has to appear somewhere to cancel the 'built-in' g in the force unit. This difficulty is eliminated in SI units because teachers and students need now remember only the 'absolute units'; i.e.

$$F \text{ (newtons)} = m \text{ (kg)} \times a \text{ (m/s}^2)$$

instead of $F \text{ (kgf)} = \dfrac{W \text{ (kg)}}{g \text{ (m/s}^2)} \times a \text{ (m/s}^2)$

The 'newtons' make things simpler both for the teacher and the taught. We must ungrudgingly change a lifetime's habits to give future generations the extremely simple, coherent and comprehensive system of units represented by SI.

All the systems of units described so far are commonly used in mechanics. They are not easy to extend to other areas of scientific study such as electricity, magnetism, thermodynamics and modern physics. Many modern scientists and engineers work in areas where these two traditional disciplines meet; hence it is necessary to ensure that the units employed in science and engineering are compatible.

3.2 SI Unit of Length: The Metre

The international prototype metre is a bar of platinum-iridium kept at 0°C and stp. It is defined as the distance between two fine lines engraved on that bar kept at the BIPM, Sevres, France. The metre defined in this way has proved quite adequate for technical and commercial purposes for over a century. However, it lacks certain properties that a standard must possess for use as a base unit for scientific purposes. These touchstones for a scientific standard are: (i) it must be indestructible, (ii) it must be reproducible to a high degree of accuracy anywhere in the world, and (iii) it must not change with time, i.e. it must be immutable. All these criteria are satisfied by the atomic standard for the metre adopted by the CIPM in 1963. The radiation is characteristic of the krypton atom and is, therefore, unchanging. It will be available as long as we can get krypton gas. Measurement of length to one part in 10^7 can be made using this atomic standard, while

one cannot read the metre bar to an accuracy higher than 10^{-5}, because the marking lines on it are thicker than this value. For all practical and commercial purposes, this atomic standard is equal to the Sevres prototype metre. The alternative standard set up in 1963 is intended to meet the growing and exacting demands of science and technology.

3.3 SI Unit of Mass: The Kilogram

What is meant here is the physicists' mass or inertial mass. It is a number which tells us what happens to an object (a mass or lump of matter) when acted upon by a force, i.e. it is a direct measure of the 'difficulty' with which a body is accelerated. This should not be confused with the physicists' concept of weight which is a force of attraction exerted by the earth on an object near its surface which we call the force of gravity. The unit of mass, called the kilogram, is the mass of a particular cylinder of platinum-iridium alloy preserved in a vault at Sevres, France, by the BIPM.

The name kilogram (kg) is not entirely appropriate for this base unit. It should be renamed but many believe that this is impracticable. Many names, including Giorgi (with G for abbreviation, as opposed to g for gram) have been suggested. The name kilogram does not come in the way of coherent calculations if one uses the power exponent convention for prefixes accurately.

3.4 SI Unit of Time: The Second

Any regularly recurring phenomenon will serve for measuring time, provided we are able to count the number of recurrences. The interval between any two successive recurrences is a unit of time (e.g. one swing of a pendulum, one cycle of current flow) and any mechanism that can count such recurrences is called a clock.

The period of rotation of the earth is a time interval which can be very precisely observed. The time interval between the successive transits of a star past an observer's celestial meridian is defined as a sidereal or star-time day. It is the time taken for one complete rotation of the earth about its axis. Both the solar day and the sidereal day have been very carefully measured and have been found to differ only slightly. One mean solar day=1.002 737 811 8868 × sidereal day. (This is one of the most accurate measurements in physics.)

Time intervals known so accurately would certainly serve as time standards except that the earth as a clock does not satisfy one of the three criteria already laid down, viz., its rotation rate is not constant with time. The exact cause for such changes in rotation time is not known. Because of these changes, the time unit was defined in 1963 in terms of a certain given year which is already past. The internationally agreed time unit is the 'ephemeris second', defined as 1/31 556 925.9747 of the tropical year ending at midnight, 31 December 1899 (the year 1900.00). An ephemeris is simply a table of positions of celestial bodies and ephemeris time is a time-measure defined from such a table. This is the second which is in use in science and technology and corresponds to the 'second' of pracical time measurement to a high degree of accuracy. In physics and electronics, we require to measure time intervals of the order of a nanosecond (10^{-9}) or less. To achieve this, we must use recurring atomic phenomena. This leads us to the concept of the atomic clock. In 1964, the CIPM set the ephemeris second at 9 192 631 770 vibrations (exactly) of a caesium (Cs^{133}) atom. This gave us a clock on a frequency standard for the measurement of very short intervals of time in research. Thus, we have defined the time unit, both from celestial and atomic measurements, these two being related by the number 9 192 631 770. Long-term experiments are now being conducted to measure any detectable differences between astronomical and atomic time.

3.5 Non-decimal Multiples of Time
Traditionally, for about 4000 years, time has been, divided in the manner that we divide it today. The sub-multiples of the day (hours,

minutes and seconds) are indirectly connected with the division of the circle. Some suggest that time measurement too should be decimalized. But, because of some grave practical difficulties, international standardising bodies have agreed to treat the existing non-decimal time units as exceptions in the otherwise decimalized SI (metric) system. A vast literature has grown during the past few centuries on calendar reform. No final, satisfactory solution has been found because the tropical year of modern astronomy is 365.242 195 days (i.e. less than 365 1/4 days) which leads to the leap year once in 4 years. The decimal sub-division of the day gives 24 hours, 14.4 minutes, 86.4 seconds. As everyone is agreed on the existing time units, in spite of its deficiencies, the problem of decimalization of time is of purely academic interest.

3.6 Linking Units of Mechanics and Electricity
Giorgi pioneered the idea that all physical units should be defined in such a manner that they are universally applicable in all branches of physics without any conversion factors when passing from mechanics to electrostatics or electrodynamics. It is like the introduction of a common currency or scientific Esparanto throughout the world.

All the applications of physics and engineering involve both 'energy' and 'power' as common quantities. In practical engineering, the unit of energy is defined as 1 joule (1 J) and that of power is 1 watt (1 W). Since ever so many instruments and machines have been designed using these units, there is no prospect of any new system coming into being utilizing other units of energy and power.

Giorgi's first postulate was to adopt 1 joule (1 J) as the unit of energy common to both mechanics and electricity. This decision has very important consequences. In mechanics, as we have already seen, the dimensions of energy are $ML^2 T^{-2}$. Again, it would be too revolutionary to define any other unit of time than 1 second (1 s). Also, for the unit of mass, only a decimal multiple of 1 gram (1 g) say 10^{μ}g and for the unit of length only a decimal multiple of 1 metre (1 m), say 10^{λ} m can be taken into consideration, μ and λ being integers since 'metre convention standards' have to be maintained. For all possible values of μ and λ we may write

$$1 \text{ J} = 10^7 \text{ ergs} = \frac{10^7 \text{g.cm}^2}{\text{s}^2} = \frac{10^3 \text{g.m}^2}{\text{s}^2} \qquad (3.1)$$

$$1 \text{ J} = \frac{10^{\mu} \text{ g } (10^{\lambda}\text{m})}{\text{s}^2}$$

i.e. $1 \text{ J} = 10^{\mu+2\lambda} \dfrac{\text{g m}^2}{\text{s}^2} \qquad (3.2)$

From (3.1) and (3.2), we get

$$\mu + 2\lambda = 3 \qquad (3.3)$$

If we wish to utilize 1 joule as the unit of energy, and decimal multiples of 1 gram and 1 metre as units of mass and length, and 1 second as a unit of time, then we have to choose according to formula (3.3) from among the possibilities listed in Table 3.2.

Undoubtedly, possibility No. 4 will be the most acceptable to all as it contains the very units defined by the international standards of mass (kg) and length (m) preserved at Servres, France. These units are also nearly those of the classical 'technical or gravitational system of units' in mechanics with the difference that it is not the kilogram force (kgf), but the kilogram mass that is defined as the base unit. This is the only point on which technologists are obliged to make some real concession. But considering that engineers and techologists have always had some trouble with their unit of force whenever they had to deal with forces other than weights, they should agree to make this concession.

The second postulate of the Giorgi system is that it is an mks system, i.e. it is based (in its purely mechanical applications) upon the three basic units of length, mass and time. The units are:

1 metre (m) for length
1 kilogram (kg) for mass
1 second (s) for time

From these three basic units, other mechanical quantities can be defined by utilizing physical

TABLE 3.2

POSSIBLE ALTERNATIVE UNITS OF ENERGY

Sl. No.	λ	μ	Unit of mass	Unit of length	Name of system
1.	-3	9	10^9 g $= 10^6$kg	10^{-3} m $= 1$ mm	
2.	-2	7	10^7 g $= 10^4$kg	10^{-2}m $= 1$ cm	MIE
3.	-1	5	10^5 g $= 10^2$kg	10^{-1}m $= 10$ cm	
4.	0	3	10^3 g $= 1$ kg	1 m $= 0.001$ km	GIORGI
5.	1	1	10 g $= 10^{-2}$ kg	10 m $= 0.01$ km	
6.	2	-1	0.1 g $= 10^{-4}$ kg	100 m $= 0.1$ km	
7.	3	-3	10^{-3}g $= 10^{-6}$kg	1000 m $= 1$ km	
8.	4	-5	10^{-5}g $= 10^{-8}$kg	10^4 m $= 10$ km	
9.	5	-7	10^{-7}g $= 10^{-10}$ kg	10^5 m $= 100$ km	
10.	6	-9	10^{-9}g $= 10^{-12}$kg	10^6 m $= 10^3$ km	
11.	7	-11	10^{-11}g $= 10^{-14}$kg	10^7 m $= 10^4$ km	MAXWELL

laws expressing these quantities in terms of units of mass, length and time, avoiding unnecessary numerical coefficients in physical laws.

$$1N = \frac{1 \, kg \times 1 \, m}{1 \, s^2}, \text{ which is called a newton (N)}$$

$$= 10^5 \text{ dynes}$$

The unit of energy, 1 joule (1 J) is defined in the Giorgi system by

$$1 \, J = 1 \, N. \, 1 \, m$$

Since $1 \, J = 10^7 \text{ ergs} = \underbrace{1 \text{ newton}}_{10^5 \text{ dynes}} \times \underbrace{1 \text{ metre}}_{10^2 \text{ cm}}$

$$= 1 \, N. \, 1 \, m = 1 \, N. \, m$$

The unit of pressure would be

$$1 \, Pa = 1 \, N/m^2$$

$$= (10 \text{ dynes/cm}^2) = 10 \, \mu \text{ bar (1 bar} = 10 \text{ Pa)}$$
$$= 1.02 \times 10^{-5} \text{ atmosphere}$$

This unit is called a 'pascal' (Pa). Other useful relations are:

$$1 \text{ bar} = 10^5 \text{ Pa} = 10^5 \text{ N/m}^2$$
$$1 \text{ kgf} = 0.98 \text{ bar}$$
$$1 \text{ bar} = 10^2 \text{ kgf/cm}$$

The unit of power is 1 watt (W)

$$1 \, W = 1 \, J/s$$

3.7 Note on the Magnitude of the Newton (N)

The newton is a convenient unit of force both for scientific and technical applications and corresponds to 0.012 kgf. In the SI system, unlike in the mks or Giorgi systems, the kg weight or kgf has to disappear. All forces have to be measured in newtons and its decimal multipliers.

The unit of work $= 1 \, J = 1 \, N. \, m$

3.8 SI Unit of Temperature

It has been internationally agreed to designate the unit of temperature as kelvin (K) instead of a degree Kelvin (°K). This unit is determined by the Carnot cycle with the temperature of the triple point of water defined as 273.16 K (exact). Both the International Practical Kelvin (K) Temperature Scale of 1960 and the International Practical Celsius (°C) Temperature Scale of 1960 are defined by a set of interpolation equations based on the reference temperatures listed in Table 3.3.

TABLE 3.3

REFERENCE TEMPERATURES

Equilibrium	K	°C
Oxygen, liquid-gas	90.18	–182.97
Water, solid-liquid (ice point)	273.15	0.00
Water, solid-liquid-gas	273.16	0.01
Water, solid-gas	373.16	100.00
Zinc, solid-liquid	692.655	419.505
Sulphur, liquid-gas	717.75	444.6
Silver, solid-liquid	1233.95	960.8
Gold, solid-liquid	1336.15	1063.0

Three important points on four important temperature scales (at normal atmospheric pressure) are given in Table 3.4, from this table

TABLE 3.4

IMPORTANT TEMPERATURES ON VARIOUS SCALES

Point	Kelvin (K)	Celsius (°C)	Fahrenheit °F	Rankine °R
Absolute zero	0.00	−273.15	−459.67	459.67
Ice point	273.15	0.00	32	491.67
Steam point	373.15	100.00	212	671.67

it is seen that one cannot keep a 'standard temperature' but only name some physical state (like the triple-point of water) to have a particular temperature accurately determined, and make comparison with it. Kelvin pointed out that by using a thermodynamic definition of the ideal Carnot cycle a definition for temperature which is quite independent of the variation in physical properties of any substance can be devised. It is this definition that has been adopted in SI in fixing absolute zero at zero K and the triple point of water at 273.16 K. This odd value had to be chosen in order to make the new temperature scale coincide with the earlier and more widely used scale on which the two important fixed points are the freezing point and boiling point of water at stp. It is to relate these two scales that one has to define $0.00 K = -273.15 °C$ (where C is Celsius, identical with the old Centigrade scale). One other condition is that the temperature intervals on both the Kelvin and Celsius scales should be the same. As the absolute temperature of the triple-point of water is accurately determined experimentally, the boiling point of water becomes $373.15 K = 100 °C$. The Celsius temperature scale has been adopted by international bodies in 1948 and has been in vogue even in non-metric countries.

The Kelvin scale does not provided a practical method of measuring temperature. This is why a number of physical states have been ascribed agreed temperatures for the purpose of calibrating temperature-measuring devices both for laboratory and industrial use (see Table 3.5).

TABLE 3.5

STANDARD CALIBRATION TEMPERATURES

Basic fixed points	°C	Other points	°C
Oxygen point	182.92	Freezing mercury	−38.87
Ice point	0.00	Freezing tin	231.9
Steam point	100.00	Freezing antimony	630.5
Sulphur point	444.6	Freezing palladium	1552.0
Silver point	960.0	Freezing tungsten	1380
Gold point	1063.0		

The kelvin is used for absolute temperature measurements for thermodynamic calculations. The temperature intervals in the Kelvin and Celsius scales are identical.

$$0 °C = 273.15 K$$

3.9 SI Units of Work, Heat and Energy

At the moment, there are ever so many units for energy, work and heat. But, in the SI system the only unit for all forms energy is the joule. However, it is most likely that the electrical power energy unit, the kilowatt hour (kW h) and, in particle physics the electron volt (eV) will persist and may never be replaced by the joule — at least in the foreseeable future. In several independent disciplines and even in the same discipline, different energy units are being employed. The worst sinner in this respect is field of heat and thermodynamics, where the following four energy units are now in use:

(i) Btu (British thermal unit)
(ii) Chu (centigrade heat unit)
(iii) Calorie (small or big)
(iv) Therm

All these may easily be replaced by the joule because they bear a simple relationships to the joule as shown below:

$$
\begin{aligned}
1 \text{ Btu} &= 1055 \quad KJ \\
1 \text{ Chu} &= 1900.4 \quad KJ \\
1 \text{ therm} &= 105.506 \text{ MJ} \\
1 \text{ calorie} &= 4.0 \quad J
\end{aligned}
$$

The electrical energy unit of

$$1 \text{ kW h} = 3.6 \times 10^6 \text{ J or } 3.6 \text{ MJ}$$

The following energy equivalence relationships are possible if the newton is used as the unit for force:

$$1 \text{ N.m} = 1 \text{ V.A.s} = 1 \text{ W s} = 1 \text{ J}$$

(Mechanical) (Electrical) (Magnetic) (Electrical)

TABLE 3.6

EXISTING HEAT ENERGY UNITS

Unit	Mass of water	temperature	gram-calories
(1) gram-calorie	1 g	1°C	1
(2) big-calorie	1 kg	1°C	1000
(3) Btu	1 lb	1°F	252
(4) Chu	1 lb	1°C	453.6
(5) Therm	10^5 lb	1°F	2.52×10^7

Table 3.6 gives the values in gram-calories of five units of heat showing that the gram-calorie is the smallest and the therm the largest unit. The calorie has no place in SI. 'Heat without calories' may look like something of an anomaly in teaching of physics in SI units !

In thermodynamics, two important quantities appear. These and their units are:

> (i) Entropy—J/K
> (ii) Specific Entropy—J/(kg K)

3.10 SI Unit of Power

The SI unit of power is the watt (W).

Power is defined as the rate of doing work. In SI, it is 1 J/s=N m/s =1 W. This unit is familiar in electricity, being the product of 1 V and 1 A. The rating of electric motors used to be in horsepower (hp), which is converted to watts by the conversion factor: 1 hp=746 W (British). The French horsepower is called *cheval vapeur* (cv)=75 kgf or nearly 736 watts. When James Watt invented his steam engine, his prospective customers, the mine owners, used to ask him: 'If I buy your engine, how many horses will it replace?' So, he experimented with a Cornish farm horse in a mine shaft and came to the conclusion that it can raise a load of 550 ft lb/second. He named this one 'horse power' and it is found to equal

746 watts in electricity. Now the hp will have to be discarded, being both a non-coherent unit and as well as a gravitational unit. All electric motors will be rated in kilowatts if the SI system is used. Since 1 kw=1000 W, 1 kw=1 1/3 hp (nearly).

3.11 SI Unit of Electric Current

The SI unit of current is the ampere (A). Every student of science and engineering has to learn about electric current at some stage or the other. Hence it is rational to have a system in which its dimension is not dependent on the equation used to define it. The latest definition of the ampere is linked to the force newton. The adoption of the ampere, an electrical quantity, as the fourth fundamental unit is a recognition of the distinctive character of electric and magnetic phenomena. Also, it simplifies relationships among the units in electricity and magnetism, electrical engineering and electronics. Previously, some ten different systems of units were in use in these fields and there was utter confusion. This confusion arose because:

(i) The relationship between electric and magnetic field properties was not fully appreciated for some time. So, separate systems called the CGS absolute electrostatic system and CGS absolute electromagnetic system were independently developed.

(ii) The physicist forced units from mechanics on electrical quantities by using Coulomb's inverse square law for magnetic poles and a similar law for electric charges, viz.,

$$F = \frac{m_1 m_2}{\mu d^2} \text{ and } F = \frac{q_1 q_1}{\varepsilon d^2}$$

Also, in these two formulae, μ and ε are each taken to be unity as they were assumed to be dimensionless.

(iii) The practical electrical engineer used another set of units called 'practical units', which are multiples of absolute cgs electrostatic and electromagnetic units. Table 3.7 summarizes the relationship between practical and absolute electrical units. The more important practical units formerly

trated in later sections in this book.

The integration of the units of mechanics with those of electricity and magnetism was first proposed by Professor Giovanni Giorgi in 1901.

TABLE 3.7

PRACTICAL, ELECTROMAGNETIC AND ELECTROSTATIC UNITS

Quantity	Practcal uniit	cgs e.m. unit	cgs e.s. unit	e.m. unit/e.s. unit
emf	1 volt	10^8 abvolts	1/300 statvolt	c
resistance	1 ohm	10^9 abohms	$1/(9 \times 10^{11})$ statohms	c^2
current	1 ampere	10^{-1} abampere	3×10^9 statamps	1/c
charge	1 coulomb	10^{-1} abcoulomb	3×10^9 statcoulombs	1/c
capacitance	1 farad	10^{-9} abfarad	9×10^{11} statfarads	$1/c^2$
inductance	1 henry	10^9 abhenry	$(1/9 \times 10^{11})$ stathenry	c^2

NOTE : $c = 3 \times 10^{10}$ cm/s, the velocity of electromagnetic waves.

were the volt, ampere, ohm, coulomb, farad, henry, joule and watt, but now in SI all these have become the main or absolute units. The original practical system was not extended to the measurement of magnetic and electric fields.

The unit of emf is now defined in a new way. 1 volt=(1 joule/1 coulomb) instead of the CGS definition, which would introduce a big factor factor (10^8). Even avoiding the factor (10^8) is a valuable advantage in electrical calculations. In SI

$$1 \text{ watt} = 1 \text{ volt} \times 1 \text{ amp}$$
$$1 \text{ joule} = 1 \text{ watt second} = 1 \text{ volt} \times 1 \text{ amp} \times 1 \text{ second}$$

Thus SI provides 'practical' units in the metric system which individually are not new. The only important new units are the newton (N), the unit of force; the weber (wb), the unit of flux; the tesla (T), the unit of flux density; and the hertz (Hz), the unit of frequency. The application of SI electrical units will be illus-

This system was accepted by the IEC in 1935 and recommended for universal adoption in one of two possible forms without specifying which. In July 1950, just one month before Giorgi's death, the IEC meeting in Paris finally decided in favour of the rationalised form (RmksA) with the ampere as the base electrical unit. (Giorgi's original proposal for the 4th base unit was 'ohm', which was later given up.) The present definition of the fundamental electrical, unit, adopted in 1948, does not depend on physical properties. The ampere is defined as that constant current which, if maintained in two straight parallel conductors of infinite length of negligible cross-section and placed one metre apart in vacuum, would produce between these conductors a force equal to 2×10^7 newtons per metre of length. The following features of the definition need attention:

(i) The newton is a unit of force (defined already).

(ii) The conductors are assumed to be of negligible cross-section so that they are exactly one metre apart. (If the conductors have any thickness, the current will be flowing across the whole of the thickness and it will not be possible to say exactly how far apart they are.)

(iii) The conductors are assumed to be placed in a vacuum because the force experienced depends also on the medium between the conductors. (For most practical purposes, the difference if they are in air is negligible.)

(iv) The conductors must be very long if the magnetic field and, hence, the force experienced is to be uniform along the whole length of the part of the wire considered.

(v) The value of 2×10^{-7} N/m for the force exerted was chosen in order to make this value of the ampere the same as in other standards which had already been in vogue for several decades.

(vi) Recent developments in physics have shown that it is advisable to replace previous standards set in terms of electrolytic effect by a standard in terms of the magnetic effect. By adopting current as a base quantity, voltage has become a derived unit.

3.12 SI Units of Luminous Intensity, Lumious Flux and Illumination

The SI unit of luminous intensity is the candela (cd) which is the luminous intensity in the direction normal to a surface of 1/600 000 square metre of a black body at the temperature of solidification of platinum at a pressure of 100 325 newtons per square metre.

The lumen (lm) is the *luminous flux* emitted within a unit solid angle of one steradian by a uniform point source of one candela. Its units are, therefore, cd. sr.

The unit of illumination is called the lux (lx). It is an illumination of one lumen per square metre and its units are lm/m². Another unit sometimes used is the phot$=10^4$ lx$=10^4$ lm/m².

From the above definitions, it will be seen that the total flux emitted by a candela in all directions is $4\pi \approx 12.57$ lumens. A 100-watt incandescent lamp emits a total flux of approximately 1260 lumens.

The unit generally employed in the fps system for illumination is the foot candle. The illumination on a surface in foot candles is calculated by the Lambert's Cosine Law:

$$L = \frac{C \cos \theta}{d^2}, \text{ where}$$

$L=$ illumination
$C=$ candle-power of the source
$d=$ distance from the source
$\theta=$ angle between the direction of the incident ray and the normal to the surface.

It is clear that 1 foot candle$=$lm/ft²
≈ 10.76 lm/m² $= 10.76$ lx.

CHAPTER FOUR

SI Units in Primary and Secondary Education

4.1 SI Units in Primary Classes

At the primary level, subjects which involve units are arithmetic and elementary science. There is no doubt that much of the teaching of units at both the primary and secondary levels is rapidly becoming out of date and needs replacement by new methods. The chief units which are used in primary schools are those of length, capacity or volume, mass and weight, area, time and money. In measuring lengths, pupils must become familiar with the metre, centimetre and millimetre. The teacher may measure the height of each pupil and record it in metres and millimetres. Similarly, water and milk may be measured in litres. The children may be encouraged to handle the litre and the decilitre. They may be asked to say how much milk or water they usually drink. Again, each pupil may be measured in a balance and his 'weight' or, more accurately, his 'mass' may be recorded. Weight as a pull of gravity, which acts on any mass including one's own body, may be explained. Unfortunately, the two concepts, 'mass' and 'weight' are often not clearly distinguished either by the teachers or pupils. This confusion can lead to considerable difficulty in teaching mechanics in later years. Introduction of SI units offers a great opportunity for clarifying the concepts and for drawing a clear distinction between the kilogram and the newton. Children can be taught the concept of 'weightlessness' by reference to space flights and photographs of astronauts. For dealing with areas, children at primary level need mainly square millimetres, square centimetres. They also need to know how many square centimetres and square millimetres are contained in a square metre (m^2). They are not really concerned with 'are' and 'hectare' at their level.

Even though the final aim is to make them think in metric (SI) units, for children now at school the following approximate conversions will be useful: 1 ft $\approx$ 30 cm; 1 yd $\approx$ 1 m (actually 1 metre is longer than a yard by about 4 inches); 1 in $\approx$ 2$\frac{1}{2}$ cm; 1 km $\approx$ 5/8 mile (or 0.6 mile); 1 gallon $\approx$ 4$\frac{1}{2}$ litres; 1 kg $\approx$ 2 lb; $\frac{1}{2}$ kg $\approx$ 16 oz; 100 gm $\approx$ 1/4 lb; 1 oz $\approx$ 30 g.

These rough-and-ready conversions may help children to think of length, volume and mass metrically. Actually, physical units in both SI and fps systems may be shown and compared. The change of emphasis from fractions to decimals must start at the primary stage. Children need to be introduced to such basic fractions as 0.5 = 1/2; 0.25 = 1/4; 0.75 = 3/4; 0.125 = 1/8.

Decimal concepts of length, area, volume

and money will simplify and unify calculations to such an extent that arithmetic will occupy a much smaller part of the curriculum than now and will leave much more time for other more modern and interesting topics.

4.2 SI Units in High School Science

At the secondary school, the subjects taught are Mathematics (arithmetic, mensuration, algebra, geometry and elementary trignometry), Physics, Chemistry, Biology, Geography, Commercial Subjects and Domestic Science.

The primary school must prepare pupils for the secondary school and the secondary school for college education or careers. Thus, the secondary schools have the responsibility of preparing pupils for intimate contact with the SI metric system. These schools will be concerned with changes in daily life which will follow from metricization, just as they had a similar task in relation to decimalization of currency fifteen years ago. Hence, it is necessary to prepare textbooks in all subjects using SI vocabularly and to re-equip classes with scientific apparatus calibrated according to the SI system. The changes to be made are largely limited to changing pounds (lb) and ounces (oz) to kilograms (kg) and grams (g), and miles, yards, feet and inches to kilometres, metres, centimetres and millimetres. Corresponding changes in area and volume measurements have also to be made. Even though, according to SI, the cm is to be eliminated, it is not possible to do so for good educational reasons: the centimetre is likely to be the most familiar unit in secondary schools, when, perhaps, instead of the 12″ foot-rule, the students will prefer a 20-cm (or 200-mm) scale or rule which they can easily carry in their pockets.

There are certain advantages to be gained in secondary schools by the introduction of SI. With the units now in vogue, teachers are often obliged to set problems using numbers which conveniently get cancelled out with conversion factors. In many of the problems set in mensuration and elementary physics, the concern is more often with conversion factors than the basic principles involved. The use of SI will correct this wrong emphasis. It will eliminate the artificial questions and will make a much smaller demand on the child's memory, which can be trained to better purpose in grasping more advanced concepts. Another major advantage is the removal of the existing artificial division between absolute and gravitational units. According to Professor M.J. Lighthill, a noted authority on 'metrication' in the UK, the greatest advantage of SI is that it is an ABSOLUTE SYSTEM and therefore bridges the existing gulf between science and engineering through technology. At present, scientists use absolute units and engineers use gravitational units and the technologists use both. By using only one system, the absolute system, a common language is forged for all fields and for the entire world.

In the teaching of science subjects, the following points need emphasis:

(i) the use of 'newton' for force *always*, reserving 'kilogram' solely for mass

(ii) the use of 'joule' for all forms of energy, reserving kW h for electrical energy only

(iii) the use of 'watt' for all forms of power, including electrical power

(iv) discarding of horsepower (hp)—British or metric

(v) the use of $kg\ m^{-3}$ as the unit of density invariably

(vi) the use of the terms 'heat capacity' and 'specific heat capacity' in place of calories in teaching heat

(vii) the use of SI units only in teaching sound, electricity, magnetism and light

4.3 Exponential Notation

To realize the benefits of the SI system fully, students need to be initiated to the use of exponential notation even at the school stage. Though industry may still use the solidus (/), e.g. 10 km/s instead of 10 km s^{-1}, the scientist should prefer the latter. For this purpose, the exponential notation together with rules for converting any number to this notation and a few elementary laws of algebra are given below. This is also called 'power-of-ten' notation. It is a shorthand method of writing very large and very small numbers. The method is based on the fact that all numbers (in decimal form) can be expressed in the form $p \times 10^n$, where p is a a number between 1 and 10 and n a positive or negative integer. A simple rule will be given for expressing any such number in this form; but, before trying to understand the rule, the student must make sure that he is conversant with the following simple mathematical and algebraic principles:

Every time the decimal point of a number is moved to a place to the right, the number is multiplied by 10; every time it is moved a place to the left the number is divided by 10; e.g. if the decimal point is moved by 4 places to the right, the number is multiplied by 10^4; if it is moved 4 places to the left the number is divided by 10^4. Problems involving $10^{\pm n}$ will arise when multiples of the base units are used. Thus,

$$(p \times 10^a) \times (q \times 10^b) = pq \times 10^{(a+b)}$$

$$(p \times 10^a) \div (q \times 10^b) = \frac{p}{q} \times 10^{(a-b)}$$

$$(p \times 10^a)^b = p^b \times 10^{ab}$$

$$\frac{1}{10^a} = 10 - a \qquad \frac{10^a}{10^a} = 10^0 = 1$$

$$\frac{p}{10^a} = p \times 10^{-a}$$

4.4 Conversion Rules

To convert any number in decimal form to the form $p \times 10^n$ where p is a number between 1 and 10 and n positive or negative:

(i) Suppose the decimal point of the given number is to be between its first and second significant figures. Let the resulting number be p.

(ii) Count the number of places by which the decimal point must be moved to the right (or left) from this new position to form the original number. This gives the index of the power of ten by which p must be multiplied (or divided) as the case may be.

(iii) If the power of 10 happens to be in the denominator, bring it to the numerator by making the sign of the index negative.

Examples
(1) $23\,8000 = 2.38 \times 10^5$
(2) $95\,000\,000 = 9.5 \times 10^7$
(3) $0.000\,016\,9 = 1.69 \div 10^5 = 1.69 \times 10^{-5}$
(4) $0.000\,000\,000\,758 = 7.58 \div 10^{10}$
$$= 7.58 \times 10^{-10}$$

4.5 Conventions for Labelling Axes on Graphs and Headings of Columns in Tables of Readings

RS 1969 gives the following convention for the labelling of graphs and the heading of columns: A symbol for a quantity, e.g. I for current, represents the product of a magnitude (the scale reading) and a unit (in terms of which the instrument is calibrated).

Thus $I = 3$ A means $I = 3 \times$ A

Hence $3 = I$ divided by A, or $3 = I/A$

A graph is a mathematical device dealing with numbers only. When the number 3 above is plotted on it, it represents I/A, and this is how the relevant axis should be a labelled. The examples shown in Fig. 4.1 illustrate this.

In the same way, a table of readings of current and potential difference recorded in order to plot the characteristic of a valve or other conductor or semi-conductor, would be headed as in Table 4.1.

When introducing this convention to junior classes it may be enough to say 'the unit is always indicated by putting its symbol after a stroke (solidus) following the symbol for the quantity being recorded or plotted'.

It is appreciated that at an elementary level this convention may be confusing. There

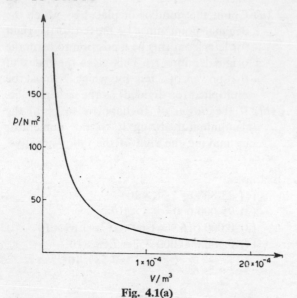

Fig. 4.1(a)

Notes: 1. Along the *x*-axis, the volume *V* is plotted in
in cubic metres (m³).
2. Along the *y*-axis the pressure *p* is plotted in
newton per square metre (N m⁻²).

TABLE 4.1

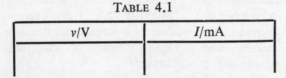

v/V	*I*/mA

NOTE: In column 1, voltage in volts (*v*) and in column 2,
the current *I* in milliamperes (mA) are shown.

remains the option of labelling the axes with the
units in words or symbols, e.g. '*V* in cubic
metres' which is understood to mean 'the
magnitude of *V* in cubic metres'.

4.6 Distinction between Italics and Roman Script in Handwriting

There may be some doubts about the difficulty
of distinguishing in handwriting between symbols
in italic letters and abbreviations for their units
in roman letters since handwriting, on the
blackboard and on paper, is rarely specifically
one or the other.

It has been suggested that the unit abbreviations might be distinguished by being under-
lined; but underlining happens to be the stan-

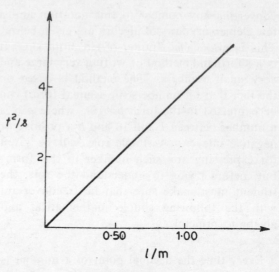

Fig. 4.1(b)

Notes: 1. Length *l* in metres (m) is plotted along the
x-axis.
2. Time *t* in seconds (s) is plotted along the
y-axis.

dard method of indicating to the printer that
matter is to be set in italics. Clearly it would
be undesirable for pupils to get used to a mis-
leading practice. It is possible on a blackboard
to use a different colour of chalk and a different
colour of ink or pencil on paper but this is most
inconvenient for general use.

In fact, the apprehension about confusion is
almost entirely unfounded for the following
reasons. A symbol for a quantity represents
both its magnitude and its unit (see paragraph
above); it is, therefore, always wrong to use a
unit symbol in conjunction with the symbol for
a quantity and for this reason instances giving
rise to confusion will not occur. Thus $V = 5$,
or $V = 5$ volt are both correct but it is wrong to
write 'the p.d. V V'.

The only time that quantity symbols and unit
abbreviations are used in close proximity is in
the labelling of graphs and the headings of
of tables of results, as shown in a preceding paragraph and if there is difficulty in avoiding
confusion, one has always the option of spelling
out the unit in full.

4.7 The Decimal Point and the Writing of Large Numbers

Two decimal signs are internationally accepted; the point placed level with the feet of the numerals, e.g. 2.1, and the comma similarly placed e.g. 2,1. The former is recommended for school use in the UK. The use of the raised point, e.g. 2·1 should be discontinued.

In order to avoid confusion with its use as a decimal sign, especially in works orginating in other countries, the comma is no longer to be used in large numbers to divide them into groups of three digits. Instead, as indicated earlier, where such division is necessary, a space may be left. Thus $299792500 \text{ m s}^{-1}$ for the speed of light should be written $299\ 792\ 500 \text{ m s}^{-1}$ and not $299,792,500 \text{ m s}^{-1}$. However, the preferred usage would be $2.997\ 925 \times 10^8 \text{m s}^{-1}$. In view of the use of the level point as a decimal sign, it should not be used to indicate a product of numbers for which the symbol $\times$ is standard.

4.8 Use of the Word 'Specific'

It has been agreed that the word *specific* used before a quantity shall always have the meaning 'per unit mass'. Thus, specific heat capacity means heat capacity per unit mass which has hitherto been known simply as 'specific heat'. It follows that the quantity so far called 'latent heat', which has always referred to unit mass of a substance must now be called 'specific latent heat'. The charge per unit mass for the electron, $- 1.758\ 196 \times 10^{11} \text{ C kg}^{-1}$, is called its specific charge. The specific charge for the proton is $9.5790 \times 10^7 \text{ C kg}^{-1}$. Another example is specific volume which is the reciprocal of density.

The term hitherto known as 'specific gravity' does not refer to unit mass and cannot now continue in use. Instead, we may use the alternative term 'relative density'. However, it is doubtful whether this concept has any value other than as a source for problems, since its use has always clearly assumed a value for the density of water. Any problems where it is used can always be done in terms of densities as such. It is, therefore, suggested that calculations be always based on densities and that the concept 'relative density' be allowed to fall into disuse.

4.9 Use of the Word 'Molar'

Strictly speaking, the word 'molar' placed before a quantity means 'per unit amount of substance', the amount being some particular amount indicated in the context. In general use, this will almost invariably mean 'per mole,' and this is understood unless some other amount is specified.

In physical chemistry and molecular physics, the introduction of the additional unit, the mole (mol), has been recommended by the International Union of Pure and Applied Physics (IUPAP), International Union of Pure & Applied Chemistry (IUPAC), and International Standards Organisation/Technical Committee 12.

The mole replaces the concept formerly known as the gramme-molecule, gramme-atom, etc., and is somewhat anomalous in being based on the gramme rather than the SI unit, the kilogramme. The mole is the amount of substance which contains as many elementary units as there are carbon atoms in 0.012 kg (exactly) of ^{12}C. The elementary units referred to may be atoms, molecules, ions, electrons or other groups of such particles. The number of entities per mole, $(6.022\ 52 \pm 0.000\ 28) \times 10^{23} \text{ mol}^{-1}$, is called the Avogadro constant.

A mole of carbon dioxide has a mass of approximately 44 g. A mole of electrons has a charge of $- (9.648\ 70 \pm 0.000\ 16) \times 10^4 \text{ C}$. The molar volume of a gas at stp is $22\ 414 \text{ cm}^3 \text{ mol}^{-1}$, or $0.022\ 414 \text{ m}^3 \text{ mol}^{-1}$.

The subscript M (in roman type) may be attached to the symbol for any quantity to indicate that it is a molar quantity.

4.10 Abbreviations for Common Words and Pharases

There are many common words and phrases for which it is convenient to have standard abbreviations. Any list of such abbreviations is of necessity somewhat arbitrary but the following are all commonly used in schools:

alternating current	a c	freezing point	f p
atomic weight	at wt	melting point	m p
boiling point	b p	molecular weight	mol wt
direct current	d c	potential difference	p d
electromotive force	e m f	relative humidity	r h
		root mean square	r m s
		ultra violet	u v
		vapour density	v d
		vapour pressure	v p

Examples

4.11 PHYSICS

DYNAMICS, STATICS AND HYDROSTATICS

Some Useful Conversion Factors

The unit of *velocity* is 1 metre per second = 1 ms^{-1} (1 mile/hour = 0.447 m/s)

The unit of *acceleration* is 1 metre per second per second = 1 ms^{-2}

The unit of *force* is 1 newton (1N) (1 N = 10^5 dynes)

The unit of *energy*, *work* and *heat* is 1 joule (1 J) (1 J = 10^7 ergs)

The unit of *power* is 1 Watt (1 W = 1 joule per second = 1 $J s^{-1}$)

The unit of *torque* is newton-metres (N m) (No distinction need be made between the units of torque and moment) (1 lb ft = 1.357 N m)

The unit of *density* is kilogram per metre cubed = 1 kg m^{-3}

The unit of *pressure* is 1 newton per metre squared = 1 N m^{-2} (1 bar == 10^5 N m^{-2}; 1 millibar = 1 mbar = 10^2 N m^{-2})

760 mm of mercury at s t p = 1 atmosphere = 1 atm = 101 325 N m^{-2}

Velocity (fps & SI)

Example 1: If a car is travelling at 30 mph, calculate its velocity in metres/second.

Solution:

$$30 \text{ miles} = 30 \times 5280 \times 12 \times 2.54 \text{ cm}$$
$$= 30 \times 5280 \times 12 \times 2.54 \times 10^{-2} \text{ m}$$
$$1 \text{ hour} = 60 \times 60 = 3600 \text{ seconds}$$
$$\text{Therefore, } v = \frac{30 \times 5280 \times 12 \times 2.54 \times 10^{-2}}{3600} = \boxed{13.4 \text{ m/s}}$$

Acceleration (fps & SI)

Example 2: A car travelling at 20 mph increases its speed at a uniform rate reaching 60 mph in 15 minutes. Calculate its acceleration in SI.

Solution:

Increase in speed	$= 60 - 20 = 40$ mph
	$= 40 \times 0.447 = 17.88$ m/s
Time taken	$= 15 \times 60 = 900$ seconds

Therefore, acceleration $= 17.88/900 \approx \boxed{0.02 \text{ m/s}^2}$

Velocity (in SI only)

Example 3: A motor car starting from rest has a uniform acceleration of 0.75 ms^{-2}. How much time will it take to attain a velocity of 54 km h^{-1}?

Solution: 54 km h^{-1} = 54/3.6 m s^{-1} = 15 m s^{-1}

$v = u + at$

$15 = 0.75 \times t$; $t = \dfrac{15}{0.75} = \boxed{20 \text{ s}}$

Note

1 km = 1000 m

1 h = 60 × 60 = 3600 s

Therefore 1 km/h = 1000/3600 = $\dfrac{1}{3.6}$ m s^{-1}

Example 4: When a car is proceeding at 72 km h^{-1}, brakes are applied causing a retardation of 2 m s^{-2}, in what time does the car stop? How far does it travel after the brakes are applied?

Solution: 72 km h^{-1} = 72/3.6 m s^{-1} = 20 m s^{-1}

$v = u + at$

$0 = 20 - 2t$ (negative sign because retardation)

$t = 20/2 = 10$ s

$v^2 = u^2 + as$

$0 = 20^2 - 2 \times 2 \times s$

$0 = 400 - 4$ s

Therefore s $= 400/4 = \boxed{100 \text{ m}}$

Motion under Gravity

Example 5: An object is projected upwards with a velocity of 4.9 m s^{-1} from a tower 98 m high.

(*i*) How high does it reach above the tower?

(*ii*) How much time does it take to reach the ground?   (Take $g = 9.8$ m s^{-2})

Solution

During the first lap of the journey from the point of projection to the point of zero velocity, the object is uniformly retarded at 9.8 m s^{-2} (moving up against gravity).   When it reaches the maximum point, it is momentarily at rest.   Using the formula: $v^2 = u^2 + 2\ as$ with $a = -9.8$ m s^{-2}

$$0 = 4.9^2 - 2 \times 9.8 \times s$$

$$s = \frac{4.9 \times 4.9}{2 \times 9.8} = 4.9/4 = \boxed{1.225 \text{ m}}$$

To travel from the point of projection to the highest point:
$$v = u + at$$
$$0 = 4.9 - 9.8\ t \text{ or} \quad \text{or } t = 4.9/9.8 = \boxed{0.5 \text{ s}}$$

The object takes the same time to return to the original point of projection and will then be moving downwards at 4.9 m s^{-1}.   So, the time from point of projection to the maximum height and back to the original height is 0.5 s + 0.5 s = 1.0 s.   After passing the point of projection, it moves *downwards* at 4.9 m s^{-1} and is now being accelerated by gravity at 9.8 m s^{-2} downwards.   Using the equation, $s = ut + \frac{1}{2} gt^2$

$$98 = 4.9\ t + \tfrac{1}{2} \times 9.8 \times t^2$$
$$20 = t + t^2 \text{ or } t^2 + t - 20 = 0$$
i.e. $$(t + 5)\ (t - 4) = 0$$

Taking the positive value, $t = 4$ s (to travel from the tower to the ground).

Therefore, total time $= 1 + 4 = 5$ seconds $= \boxed{5 \text{ s}}$

Simple Pendulum

Example 6: If a pendulum has a period of 2.0 s on the earth, what would be its period on the moon, where the acceleration due to gravity is one-sixth of 'g' on earth.

Solution: Formula: $T = 2\pi \sqrt{\dfrac{l}{g}}$

On earth $T = 2.0$ s
On the moon, let the period of the pendulum be T_1 seconds

Therefore, $2 = 2\pi \sqrt{l/g}$

$$T_1 = 2\pi \sqrt{\frac{l}{g/6}} \text{ or, } \frac{T_1}{2} = \sqrt{6}$$

$$T_1 = 2\sqrt{6} = 2 \times 2.444 = 4.888 \text{ s}$$

Therefore, the period of the pendulum on the moon = 4.888 s or say $\boxed{4.90 \text{ s}}$

Newton's Laws of Motion

Example 7: Find the acceleration of a body on a mass of 20 kg when it is subjected to a horizontal force of 100 N (*i*) if it can move along a smooth horizontal surface; and (*ii*) if it can move along a rough horizontal table, having a frictional resistance of 70 N.

Solution: (*i*) $F=ma$

UNITS: F, force, in N
           m, mass, in kg
           a, acceleration, in m s^{-2}

$100 = 20 \, a$. Therefore, $a = 100/20 = 5$ m s^{-2}

(*ii*) $F = ma$ but F is the *net force* $= 100 - 70 = 30$ N

Therefore, $30 = 20 \times a$

Therefore, $a = 30/20 = \boxed{1.5 \text{ m s}^{-2}}$

Example 8: A rocket of mass 750 Mg has motors giving a thrust of 10^6 kg f. Find the acceleration at lift off (take $g = 9.8$ m s^{-2}).

Solution: The forces acting on the rocket are:
           (*i*)   thrust acting upwards
           (*ii*)   its own weight (force) acting downwards

Therefore, the net or resultant force
$$= 1000 \times 10^6 \, g - 750 \times 10^6 \, g = 250\,000 \times 9.8 \text{ N}$$

$F = ma$

$$250\,000 \times 9.8 = 750\,000 \times a$$

$$a = \frac{250\,000 \times 9.8}{750\,000} = 9.8/3 = \boxed{3.3 \text{ m s}^{-2}}$$

Example 9: A projectile of mass 100 g travelling at 1600 m s^{-1} hits a movable target of 10 kg, which is at rest. Both the target and projectile move on together after the impact. Find: (*i*) the momentum of the projectile (*ii*) the combined velocity, immediately after the impact.

Solution: (*i*)   momentum $= m \times v$
           100 g $= 0.1$ kg

           momentum $= 0.1 \times 1600 = \boxed{160 \text{ N s}}$

        Units: Momentum in N s
                 m, mass, in kg
                 v, velocity, in m s^{-1}

(ii) According to the principle of conservation of momentum, momentum before impact=
momentum after impact

$m_1 v_1 + m_2 \times 0 = (m_1 + m_2) \times v$

where m_1, is the mass of the projectile (in kg), v_1 the velocity of the projectile in m s^{-1}
before impact, m_2 the mass of the target (in kg), and v the common velocity after the
impact in m s^{-1}

Then $0.100 \times 1600 + 0 = (0.100 + 10) \times v$

Therefore, $v = 160/10.1 \approx \boxed{15.84 \text{ m s}^{-1}}$

Example 10: A metal sphere of mass 1 kg is thrown against a wall with a velocity of 4 m s^{-1}. The
sphere rebounds with a velocity of 1 m s^{-1}. If the time of impact is one millisecond, find
the average force experienced by the sphere during the impact.

Solution: Force = rate of change of momentum (Newton's second law)
= Change of momentum/time of impact
= $[1 \times 4 - (-1 \times 1)]/0.001 = 5/0.001$ N

Note: (-1×1) because the sphere rebounds in the opposite direction and momentum is a vector
quantity.

Therefore, force = $\boxed{5000 \text{ N}}$

Friction

Example 11: A metal block, resting on a horizontal surface, has a mass of 2 kg and a mass of
0.5 kg rests on top of the block. A horizontal force of 8.16 N just makes the block slip.
(i) Find the coefficient of friction.
(ii) What is the frictional force when the horizontal force applied to the block is 5.00 N ?

Solution: The total weight = 2.5×9.8 N = 24.5 N
Therefore, normal reaction R = 24.5 N
The limiting frictional force F is 8.16 N
Therefore, coefficient of friction = (limiting frictional force)/(normal reaction)

= $8.16/24.5 = \boxed{0.33}$

Since the frictional force can have any value up to the limiting value, the answer is $\boxed{5.00 \text{ N}}$

Work, Energy and Power

Example 12: Find the work done in lifting a mass of 5 kg through a height of 10 m.

Solution: Formula: $W = F \times s$
$F = m \times g \ (g = 9.8 \text{ m s}^{-2})$

Units: W, work done in J
　　　 F, force in N
　　　 s, distance moved along the line of action of the force in m
　　　 $W = 5 \times 10 \times 9.8$

　　　　　$= \boxed{490 \text{ J}}$

Example 13:   A bullet of mass 20 g moving with a velocity of 500 m s^{-1} penetrates a fixed
　　　target.   Find the depth of penetration, if the average resistive force offered by the target is
　　　10 k N.

Solution: The kinetic energy of the bullet $= \frac{1}{2} mv^2 = \frac{1}{2} \times (20/1000) \times 500^2 = 2500$ J
　　　　　Units: m, mass in kg
　　　　　　　 v, velocity in m s^{-1}
This kinetic energy is used up in doing work against the resistive force of the target.   Let s be the
　　　depth of penetration (in metres).

$$F \times s \quad = \quad 2500 \text{ J}$$
$$10000 \times s = \quad 2500$$

Therefore, $s = 2500/10000 = \boxed{0.25 \text{ m}}$

Example 14:   A lift carries 100 people of average mass 60 kg to a height of 6 m in one minute.
　　　Find the power required.

Solution: Work done $= F \times s = 100 \times 60 \times 9.8 \times 6$ J

　　　Power　　　$=$　rate of doing work, i.e .work done per second

　　　　　　　　$= \dfrac{100 \times 60 \times 9.8 \times 6}{60}$

　　　　　　　　$= 5880$ W or $\boxed{5.88 \text{ kW}}$

Note on Spring Balances

A spring balance can measure the *weight* of a body ($m \times g$) at that place while a beam balance.
compares *masses* only.   Hitherto, this distinction was not being adequately emphasized.   When
SI units are introduced for teaching science, *mass* and *weight* need to be clearly differentiated.
To familiarize students with newtons and kg f, it may be useful to develop spring balances with
dual scales marked in newtons and kg f.   For use in the secondary schools, it is sufficiently accurate
to use a value of g $\approx$ 10 m/s^2 for graduating the scales.   Six spring balances of the ranges listed
in Table 4.2 with dual scales will serve the purpose.

TABLE 4.2

SCALES FOR DUAL BALANCES

Scale (newtons)	Scale (kg f)
1. 0 − 18 × 0.2	0 − 1.8 × 0.02
2. 0 − 40 × 0.5	0 − 4.5 × 0.05
3. 0 − 80 × 1.0	0 − 9.0 × 0.10
4. 0 − 230 × 2.0	0 − 25.0 × 0.20
5. 0 − 400 × 5.0	0 − 45.0 × 0.50
6. 0 − 950 × 10.0	0 − 100 × 1.00

Moments and Centre of Gravity

Example 15: Weights W and S are suspended at B and C from a light beam $ABCD$ attached to spring balances at A and D respectively. If the readings on the balances are 4 kg f and 10 kg f respectively, and if $AB = 40$ cm, $BC = 40$ cm, $CD = 20$ cm, calculate W and S.

Solution: Since it is a light beam, ignore its weight.

Equations: $\qquad W + S = 4 + 10 = 14$ kg f $\hfill$ (1)

$\qquad\qquad$ Taking moments about A,

$$W \times 40 + S \times 80 - 10 \times 100 = 0$$

or $\qquad 4\,W \times 8\,S = 100 \hfill$ (2)

$\qquad\qquad$ Taking moments about D

$$-4 \times 100 + W \times 60 + S \times 20 = 0$$

$$6\,W + 2\,S = 40 \hfill (3)$$

$\qquad$ Multiplication of (1) by (2) gives:

$$2\,W + 2\,S = 28 \hfill (4)$$

$\qquad$ Subtracting (4) from (3): $4\,W = 12$ kg f or $W = 3$ kg f

$\qquad\qquad$ Therefore, $2 \times 3 + 2\,S = 28$ or

$$2\,S = 22 \text{ or } S = 11 \text{ kg f}$$

$$\boxed{\text{Thus, } W = 3 \text{ kg f and } S = 11 \text{ kg f}}$$

Example 16: In the above example, calculate the readings of the two spring balances, when $W = 5$ kg f and $S = 8.0$ kgf.

Solution: Let T_1 and T_2 be the spring balance readings at A and D.

$$T_1 + T_2 = 5 + 8 = 13$$

Taking moments about A, $5 \times 40/100 + 8.0 \times 80/100 - T_2 = 0$

$$2 + 6.4 = T_2 \text{ or } T_2 = 8.4 \text{ kg f}$$

Therefore, $T_1 = 13 - 8.4 = 4.6$ kg f

$$\boxed{T_1 = 4.6 \text{ kg f and } T_2 = 8.4 \text{ kgf}}$$

Machines: Screw Jack

Example 17 : A screw jack with a pitch of 4 mm and an arm of 56 cm is used to lift a motor car of 880 kg. If the efficiency of the jack is 20%, find the effort to be applied to the end of the arm (take $g = 10$ m s^{-2}).

Solution :

Velocity ratio of the screw

= Circumference of arm/pitch of screw

= 2 π × 0.56/0.004

= 2 × 22 × 0.56/7 × 0.004

= 880

Efficiency = mechanical advantage (*MA*)/velocity ratio × 100

Therefore, 20 = *MA*/880 × 100

Therefore, *MA* = 20 × 880/100 = 176

Since *MA* = Load/effort, and Load = 880 × 10 N

176 = 880 × 10/effort, or effort = 880 × 10/176 = $\boxed{\textit{50} \text{ N (or nearly 5 kg f)}}$

Density and Relative Density

TABLE 4.3

DENSITIES AND RELATIVE DENSITIES OF SOME SOLIDS AND LIQUIDS IN SI UNITS

Substance	Density (kg/m³)	Density (g/cm³ or tonnes/m³)	Relative Density (pure number)
Aluminium	2700	2.70	2.70
Balsa wood	200	0.2	0.2
Brass	8400	8.4	8.4
Copper	8930	8.93	8.93
Cork	240	0.24	0.24
Glass	2500	2.5	2.5
Glycerine	1300	1.3	1.3
Gold	19320	19.32	19.32
Ice	920	0.92	0.92
Iron	7870	7.87	7.87
Lead	11370	11.37	11.37
Marble	2600	2.6	2.6
Mercury	13560	13.56	13.56
Methylated spirit	830	0.83	0.83
Osmium	22500	22.5	22.5
Paraffin oil	800	0.8	0.8
Paraffin wax	880	0.88	0.88
Petrol	800	0.8	0.8
Platinum	21450	21.45	21.45
Sand	2630	2.63	2.63
Sea-water	1030	1.03	1.03

NOTE : (1) The unit of density in SI is 1 kg/m while the unit of density in cgs is 1 g/cm³; to convert the density in cgs to SI, multiply by 1000 and express as kg/m³.

(2) Density in tonnes/m, (where 1 metric ton or tonne (t) = 1000 kg is the same as in grams/cm³.

(3) Relative density (a pure number) is the same as the number part of the density in the cgs system. With the introduction of SI, the term specific gravity will be dropped.

TABLE 4.4

VARIATION OF DENSITY OF WATER WITH TEMPERATURE

°C	1 (kg/m³)	°C	1 (kg/m³)
− 12	997.264	10	999.700
− 10	997.907	15	999.101
− 8	998.473	20	998.206
− 6	998.948	25	997.047
− 4	999.352	30	995.650
− 2	999.645	35	994.036
0	999.840	40	992.220
2	999.940	45	970.212
4	999.972	50	988.042
6	999.940	55	985.702
8	999.849	60	983.212
10	999.700	65	980.562

NOTES : (1) For all practical purposes, the density of water at standard atmospheric pressure (101 325/N m⁻²) may be taken as 1000 kg/m³.

(2) The above table clearly shows the anomolous expansion of water, viz. the maximum density is at 4° C=999.972 ∼ 1000 kg/m

(3) At pressures other than atmospheric, the density of water alters slightly owing to the finite value of its bulk modulus at various temperatures.

Example 18 : A laboratory is 15 m long, 8 m wide and 4 m high. What is the mass of the air enclosed in the room if the density of air is 1.23 kg m⁻³?

Solution : Volume of the laboratory = $15 \times 8 \times 4 = 480$ m³
　　　　　　Density, by definition = mass per unit volume
　　　　　　　　i. e. d = density in kg m⁻³
　　　　　　　　　　mass in kg; volume in m³
Therefore, mass　= $1.23 \times 480 = 590.4$ kg

Therefore, the mass of the enclosed air = $\boxed{590.4 \text{ kg}}$

Example 19 : Find the density of mixture of 7.5×10^{-3} m³ of water of density 1000 kg m⁻³ and 4.5×10^{-3} m³ of alcohol of density 800 kg m⁻³.

Solution : $d = \dfrac{m}{v}$

The mass of water　　　=　$v \times d$
　　　　　　　　　　=　volume of water × density of water
　　　　　　　　　　=　$7.5 \times 10^{-3} \times 1000 = 7.5$ kg
The mass of alcohol　　=　volume of alcohol × density of alcohol
　　　　　　　　　　=　$4.5 \times 10^{-3} \times 800 = 3.60$ kg

Therefore,

total mass of water and alcohol	=	$7.5 + 3.6 = 11.1$ kg
total volume of water and alcohol	=	$(7.5 \times 10^{-3} + 4.5 \times 10^{-3})$ m³
	=	12×10^{-3} m³

Density of mixture = mass of mixture/volume of mixture

$$= 11.1/(12 \times 10^{-3})$$
$$= 0.925 \times 10^3$$
$$= \boxed{925 \text{ kg m}^{-3}}$$

Density Bottle

Example 20 : A density bottle has a mass of 20.0 g when empty, 60.0 g when full of water and 52.0 g when full of paraffin. Find the density of paraffin.

Solution : mass of bottle + water	=	60.0 g
mass of bottle alone	=	20.0 g
Therefore, mass of water	=	40.0 g
Mass of bottle + paraffin	=	52.0 g
mass of bottle alone	=	20.0 g
Therefore, mass of paraffin	=	32.0 g
The volume of paraffin and water are the same,		
therefore, relative density of paraffin	=	32.0/40.0
	=	0.8 in relation to water, whose density
	=	1000 kg m⁻³
Therefore, density of paraffin	=	0.8×1000 kg m⁻³
	=	$\boxed{800 \text{ kg m}^{-3}}$

Archimedes Principle

When a body is partially or wholly immersed in a fluid, its apparent loss of weight is equal to the weight of fluid displaced.

The following are deduced from this statement:

(*i*) wt. of a body in air — wt. in a fluid = wt. of fluid displaced
   = volume of solid × density of fluid × g

(*ii*) If an object floats, its *weight* in the fluid is zero, which means
   wt. in air = wt. of fluid displaced
     = volume of solid immersed × density of fluid × g

(*iii*) If a body of volume V and density d floats in water, with a volume v below the surface, then
   $V \times d \times g = v \times 1000 \times g$ (because density of water = 1000 kg m⁻³)
   or $v/V = d/1000$

Example 21 :   A block of wood measuring 10 cm $\times$ 2 cm $\times$ 2 cm floats in water with 7 cm of its length submerged.

(i)   What is the volume of the block?

(ii)   What is the volume of water displaced ?

(iii)   What is the mass of the block ?

(iv)   What is the density of the wood ?

(v)   What additional mass would just sink the block ?

(vi)   The same block floats in a solution of copper sulphate with 6 cm of its length submerged. What is the density of copper sulphate solution ?

Solution :   (i)   Volume of the block$=10\times2\times2=$ $\boxed{40 \text{ cm}^3}$

(ii)   Volume of water displaced$=7\times2\times2=$ $\boxed{28 \text{ cm}^3}$

(iii)   *Mass of the block*
Mass of the block = mass of water displaced
= mass of 28 cm^3 of water

$$= \boxed{28 \text{ g } or \text{ } 28\times10^{-3} \text{ kg}}$$

(iv)   *Density of wood*
$d =$ (mass/volume) $= 28$ g/40 cm^3

$$= \boxed{0.7 \text{ g/cm}^3 \text{ } or \text{ } 700 \text{ kg m}^{-3}}$$

(v)   What additional weight would just sink the block ?

Upthrust $= 40 - 28 = \boxed{12 \text{ g}}$

(vi)   density of body/density of liquid = length submerged in the liquid/full length = 6/10 $= 0.7/d$ liquid

Therefore, d liquid $= \dfrac{0.7 \times 10}{6} = 1.16$ g/cm^3

Density of copper sulphate solution$= \boxed{1160 \text{ kg m}^{-3}}$

Example 22

Prove that $v/V = d/D$, where

d =   density of solid (kg m^{-3})

D =   density of liquid (kg m^{-3})

v =   submerged volume of the body (m^3)

V =   Volume of the whole body (m^3)

Principles involved

(*i*) Mass of liquid displaced = volume of liquid displaced
[(*v*) × density of liquid (*D*)]
(*ii*) Mass of floating body = entire volume of floating body (*V*)×density of the body (*d*)
= *V* × *d*

Upthrust = wt. of floating body = wt. of liquid displaced
V × *d* × *g* = *v* × *D* × *g*
or *V* × *d* = *v* × *D*
v/*V* = *d*/*D*

Example 23 : When a given hydrometer floats in fresh water 9/10 of its volume is immersed. In milk 90/103 of its volume is immersed. Find the relative density of the milk.

Solution : Let the volume of the hydrometer = *V* m³
Weight of this volume of fresh water (*W*)
= (9/10) *V* × 1000 × *g* × 1 N
W = *mgsV*
This is, of course, also the weight of the hydrometer. Similarly, in milk, with a relative density of *s*, weight of milk displaced is: (90/103) *V* × *s* × 1000 × *g*, which is also the weight of the hydrometer.
Hence, (90/103) *V* × *s* × 1000 × *g* = (9/10) *V* × 1000 × *g* × 1

or *s* = (9/10) × (103/90) = 103/100 = $\boxed{1.03}$

Example 24 . A hydrometer with a mass of 39 g floats in water with 6 cm of its stem above the surface. When floating in a liquid of density 1300 kg m⁻³, 12 cm of the stem is above the surface. What is the cross-sectional area of the uniform stem?

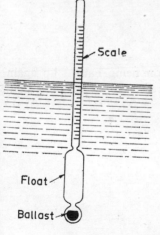

Scale

Float

Ballast

Fig. 4.2

Solution:
Let *a* be the area of the uniform stem of the hydrometer in cm². Since the liquid is more dense than water, the hydrometer rises further by a distance of 6 cm. This additional volume = area of cross-section × length = *a* × 6 cm³ (*a* in cm²).
If the volume immersed in water is *V* cm³ then the volume immersed in liquid is (*V* − 6*a*), the weight of hydrometer = weight of liquid displaced. Therefore, mass of hydrometer = mass of liquid displaced.

Mass of water	=	volume × density
39 *g*	=	0.039 kg
because 1 cm³	=	10⁻⁶ m³
(39/1000) kg	=	*V* × 1000 × 10⁻⁶
Hence, *V*	=	39 cm³
mass of liquid displaced	=	volume × density

Hence, 0.039 $\qquad = (V - 6a) \times 10^{-6} \times 1300$

$\qquad\qquad 39 \qquad\qquad = (39 - 6a) \times 10^{-6} \times 1300 \times 1000$

$\qquad\qquad 39 \qquad\qquad = (39 - 6a) \times 1.3$

$\qquad\qquad (39/1.3) \qquad = 39 - 6a$

or $\qquad\qquad 6a \qquad\qquad = 39 - (39/1.3) = 39 (1 - 1/1.3)$

$$= 39 \; \frac{(1.3 - 1)}{1.3}$$

$$= \frac{39 \times 0.3}{1.3} = 30 \times 0.3 = 9$$

$\qquad\qquad a \qquad\qquad = (9/6) = \boxed{1.5 \text{ cm}^2}$

Example 25 :   The height of a mercury barometer at s t p is 760 mm (= 0.76 m). Given ρ, density of mercury, as 13 595.1 kg m^{-3} and $g = 9.806\ 65$, find the atmospheric pressure in N m^{-2}.

Solution :

Atmospheric pressure $\qquad\qquad = \quad 0.76 \times 13\ 595.1 \times 9.806\ 65$

$$= \boxed{101\ 325 \text{ N m}^{-2}}$$

NOTE : (1) This is the value for normal atmospheric pressure accepted in SI. It is in absolute units (newtons/metre^2 or N m^{-2}).

(2) An 'inch of water', a 'foot of water', a 'millimetre of water' — all these now are obsolete units. Even mm of water is a *non-coherent* pressure unit (= 1 kg f/m^2) and hence not recommended for use.

$\qquad$ 1 in of H_2O $\qquad \approx \qquad$ 249.089 N m^{-2}

$\qquad$ 1 ft of H_2O $\qquad \approx \qquad$ 2989.07 N m^{-2}

$\qquad$ 1 in of Hg $\qquad \approx \qquad$ 3386.39 N m^{-2}

Example 26 :   A 60-cm sounding tube is lowered into the sea and, on being hauled up again, 40 cm are found to be discoloured. Find the depth of the water. (Pressure of depth of 10.36 m of sea water = 1 atmosphere.)

Solution :   Initially pressure $\qquad = \qquad$ 1 atmosphere

$\qquad\qquad\qquad$ volume $\qquad\qquad = \qquad$ 60 units

Finally the volume of gas $\qquad = \qquad$ 60 − 40 = 20 units

Let pressure of gas be P (atmosphere)

$$1 \times 60 = P \times 20 \text{ or } P = \frac{60}{20} = 3 \text{ atmospheres}$$

Of these 3 atmospheres, 1 atmosphere is due to atmospheric pressure at the surface of the water, 2 atmospheres were added by the water.   Therefore

$\qquad$ Depth of water $\qquad\qquad = \qquad$ 2 × 10.36 m

$$= \boxed{20.72 \text{ m}}$$

Example 27 : The tube of a faulty barometer containing a little air above the mercury projects 80 cm above the level of the reservoir. The inside cross-section of the tube is 1 cm². When the atmospheric pressure is 76 cm of Hg, the barometer reading is 72 cm. What will be the atmospheric pressure when the barometer is taken down a mine and reads 74 cm?

Solution : The volume of air = $(80 - 72) = 8$ cm². Its pressure = $76 - 72 = 4$ cm of Hg.

Let x be the atmospheric pressure when the faulty barometer reads 74 cm. The new volume of air = $80 - 74 = 6$ cm and the pressure of this air = $(x - 74)$ cm of Hg.

Therefore, $p_2 \times v_2 = 6 (x - 74)$

Because $p_1 v_1 = p_2 v_2$

               $p_1 v_1 = 4 \times 8 = 32$ units

Therefore, $32 = 6 (x - 74)$ or $32 = 6 x - 444$ or $6 x = 476$

Therefore, $x = (476/6) = 79\ 1/3$ cm

$$= 79.33 \text{ cm} = \boxed{793.3 \text{ mm of Hg}}$$

NOTE : The above examples have clearly brought out the point that *any convenient units* can be used for *pressure* and *volume* provided that the units for p_2 are the same as those for p_1 and that the units for v_2 are the same as those of v_1.

HEAT

Temperature ·   1 kelvin = 1K (do not write ˚K)

                  1 degree Celsius = 1 °C

                  t °C = $(t + 273.15)$ K

Quantity of heat: 1 joule = 1 J

Heat capacity: 1 joule per kelvin = 1 J K⁻¹

Specific heat capacity :   1 joule per kilogram per kelvin = 1 J kg⁻¹ K⁻¹

Specific latent heat: 1 joule per kilogram = 1 J kg⁻¹

Rate of supply of heat: ·   1 watt = 1 W = 1 joule per second = 1 J s⁻¹

NOTE : In SI, the term, *'specific heat'* is replaced by *'specific heat capacity'*, *'latent heat'* is replaced by *'specific latent heat'* and *'power'* is replaced by *'rate of supply of heat'*.

Heat Capacity and Specific Heat Capacity

(i) *By Method of Mixtures*

Example 28 :   0.053 kg of turpentine at 80° C is mixed with 0.060 kg of water at 20° C in a copper calorimeter of mass 0.091 kg. Find the final temperature.

Solution : Let t be the final temperature in °C.

Heat (lost or gained) by water = mass × specific heat capacity × temperature change

Units: Mass in kg
        Specific heat capacity in J kg K^{-1}
        Temperature change in K or °C
Heat gained by vessel = heat capacity × temperature change

TABLE 4.5

SPECIFIC HEAT CAPACITIES

Substance	Specific heat capacity (in J kg^{-1} K^{-1})
Water	4200
Copper	380
Aluminlum	875
Methylated spirit	2500
Turpentine	180ᴜ
Mercury	140
Lead	130
Silver	234
Zinc	387

Units : Heat capacity in J K^{-1}
         Temperature change in K or °C
Now, heat lost by hot turpentine = heat gained by cold water + vessel
The hot turpentine starts at 80 °C and ends at temperature t.
The cold water and vessel start at 20 °C and end at temperature t.
Therefore

$$0.053 \times 1800 \times (80 - t) = 0.06 \times 4200 \times (t - 20) + 0.091 \times 380 \times (t - 20)$$
$$95.4 (80-t) \quad = \quad 252 (t - 20) + 34.58 (t - 20)$$
$$381.98 \, t \quad = \quad 7632 + 5040 + 691.6$$
$$381.98 \, t \quad = \quad 13363.6$$

Therefore, t = 34.97 or say (35 °C)

(ii) By Electrical Heating

Example 29 :   0.20 kg of alcohol is contained in a vessel of heat capacity 80 J K^{-1}. When heated for 9 minutes by a 50 W immersion heater, the temperature rises from 25 °C to 75° C. Calculate the specific heat capacity of alcohol.

Solution

Assumtion: The heat energy gained by alcohol and vessel = electrical energy supplied.

Heat gained by alcohol   =   mass × specific heat capacity × temperature change
Heat gained by vessel   =   heat capacity × temperature change
The electric energy supplied   =   power × time (in seconds)

Let C be the specific heat capacity of alcohol, then

$$0.20 \times C \times (75 - 25) + 80 \times (75 - 25) = 50 \times 9 \times 60$$
$$0.20 \times C \times 50 + 80 \times 50 = 50 \times 540$$
$$0.2\,C + 80 = 540$$
$$0.2\,C = 460$$
$$\text{or } C = (460/0.2) = \boxed{2300 \text{ J kg}^{-1} \text{ K}^{-1}}$$

Specific Latent Heat

Data: Specific latent heat of *fusion of ice* $= 336\,000$ J kg^{-1} $= 336 \times 10^3$ J kg^{-1} $= 336$ k J kg^{-1}

Specific latent heat of *vaporisation of water:* $= 2\,250\,000$ J kg^{-1} $= 2.25 \times 10^6$ J kg^{-1} $= 2.25$ M J kg^{-1}

Specific heat capacity of water $= 4200$ J kg K $= 4.2 \times$ k Jk g^{-1} K^{-1}

(i) By Method of Mixtures

Example 30 : When 0.005 kg of ice at 0 °C is added to 0.020 kg of warm water at 30 °C, the final temperature attained is 8 °C. Calculate the specific latnet heat of fusion of ice.

Solution : Heat is gained by ice in two stages :

   (*i*) it melts;

  (*ii*) the 0.005 kg of water is formed at 0°C and then rises to 8°C. The warm water loses heat in cooling from 30 °C to 8 °C. Heat gained by ice-cold water = mass $\times$ specific heat capacity $\times$ temperature change

Heat lost by warm water = mass $\times$ specific heat capacity $\times$ temperature change

Let the specific latent heat of ice be L.

Since heat gained by ice = heat lost by warm water

$$0.005\,L + 0.005 \times 4200 \times 8 = 0.020 \times 4200 \times (30 - 8)$$

Hence, $L = 336\,000$ J kg^{-1} $= 336$ k J kg^{-1}

(ii) By Electrical Method

Example 31 : An immersion heater takes 268.8 s to heat 0.40 kg of water from 20 °C to boiling point. How much longer will it take to boil 0.01 kg of the water.

Solution : Let P be the power of the coil in watts (W).

Electrical energy produced during 268.8 s $= P \times 268.8$ J

This energy heats 0.40 kg of water from 20 °C to 100 °C.

Heat energy gained by water in J $\qquad = $ mass $\times$ specific heat capacity $\times$ temperature change
$$= 0.40 \times 4200 \times 80$$

Therefore, $P \times 268.8 = 0.40 \times 4200 \times 80$ (1)

Let the time required to boil 0.01 kg of water be t seconds (s).

The heat energy required = mass $\times$ specific latent heat
$$P \times t = 0.01 \times 2.25 \times 10^6 \qquad\qquad\qquad (2)$$

Dividing equation (2) by equation (1) :

$$\frac{P \times t}{P \times 268.8} = \frac{0.01 \times 2.25 \times 10^6}{0.40 \times 4200 \times 80}$$

$$\text{Therefore,} \quad t = \frac{0.01 \times 2.25 \times 10^6 \times 268.8}{0.40 \times 4200 \times 80}$$

$$= \frac{2.25 \times 10^6 \times 2.688}{32 \times 42 \times 10^2} = \boxed{45 \text{ s}}$$

Expansion of Solids

TABLE 4.6

COEFFICIENTS OF LINEAR EXPANSION OR LINEAR EXPANSIVITY (symbol : α)

Metal	Value of α
Aluminium	$0.000\,024\ \text{K}^{-1} = 24 \times 10^{-6}\ \text{K}^{-1} = 24 \times 10^{-6}\ {}^{\circ}\text{C}^{-1}$
Brass	$0.000\,020\ \text{K}^{-1} = 20 \times 10^{-6}\ \text{K}^{-1} = 20 \times 10^{-6}\ {}^{\circ}\text{C}^{-1}$
Copper	$0.000\,017\ \text{K}^{-1} = 17 \times 10^{-6}\ \text{K}^{-1} = 17 \times 10^{-6}\ {}^{\circ}\text{C}^{-1}$
Iron	$0.000\,012\ \text{K}^{-1} = 12 \times 10^{-6}\ \text{K}^{-1} = 12 \times 10^{-6}\ {}^{\circ}\text{C}^{-1}$
Steel	$0.000\,011\ \text{K}^{-1} = 11 \times 10^{-6}\ \text{K}^{-1} = 11 \times 10^{-6}\ {}^{\circ}\text{C}^{-1}$
Gold	$0.000\,014\ \text{K}^{-1} = 14 \times 10^{-6}\ \text{K}^{-1} = 14 \times 10^{-6}\ {}^{\circ}\text{C}^{-1}$
Silver	$0.000\,019\ \text{K}^{-1} = 19 \times 10^{-6}\ \text{K}^{-1} = 19 \times 10^{-6}\ {}^{\circ}\text{C}^{-1}$
Lead	$0.000\,029\ \text{K}^{-1} = 29 \times 10^{-6}\ \text{K}^{-1} = 23 \times 10^{-6}\ {}^{\circ}\text{C}^{-1}$
Tin	$0.000\,023\ \text{K}^{-1} = 23 \times 10^{-6}\ \text{K}^{-1} = 23 \times 10^{-6}\ {}^{\circ}\text{C}^{-1}$

Example 32 : An aluminium panel is 5 m $\times$ 3 m. What is the contraction in area, if its temperature falls by 20 °C?

Solution : Change in area $=$ A_1 βt

If α is the coefficient of linear expansion (or linear expansivity), then, $\beta = 2\alpha$

$\alpha =$ for aluminium $= 24 \times 10^{-6}\ {}^{\circ}\text{C}^{-1}$

$\beta =$ for aluminium $= 2 \times 24 \times 10^{-6}\ {}^{\circ}\text{C}^{-1} = 48 \times 10^{-6}\ {}^{\circ}\text{C}^{-1}$

Units : $A_1 =$ initial area in m^2

$\beta =$ coefficient of superficial expansion (or superficial expansivity) in K^{-1}

$t =$ temperature change in K or °C

Contraction $=$ change in area

$$= 5 \times 3 \times 48 \times 10^{-6} \times 20 \ = 300 \times 48 \times 10^{-6} \ = 144 \times 10^{-4}\ \text{m}^2 \ = \boxed{0.014\,4\ \text{m}^2}$$

Expansion of Liquids

Example 33 :   A glass bottle full of mercury at 12 °C contains 506.732 g of Hg.   When heated to 100 °C the bottle contains 500.00 g of Hg.   Find the coefficient of real expansion of Hg if the coefficient of linear expansion of glass is 9×10^{-6} K^{-1}.

Solution

$$\left.\begin{array}{l}\text{Coefficient of apparent} \\ \text{expansion of mercury}\end{array}\right\} = \frac{\text{mass expelled}}{(\text{mass remaining in bottle} \times \text{temperature change})}$$

$$= \frac{506.732 - 500.000}{500 \times (100 - 12)}$$

$$= 6.732/(500 \times 88) = 6.732/44\,000 = 0.000\,1530 \text{ K}^{-1}$$

Coefficient of real expansion = coefficient of apparent expansion + coefficient of cubical expansion of the bottle

If α is the coefficient of linear expansion of glass bottle, then γ, the coefficient of cubical expansion of glass = 3 α.

Therefore, γ = $3 \times 9 \times 10^{-6}$ = 27×10^{-6} =   0.000 027

Therefore, coefficient of real expansion = 0.000 1530 + 0.000 027

$$= \boxed{0.000\,180 \text{ K}^{-1}}$$

Example 34 :   A fixed mass of gas at constant pressure has a volume of 576 cm^3 at 15 °C.   Find its volume (*i*) at 0 °C and (*ii*) at 100 °C.

Solution :   Formula: $\dfrac{pV}{T}$ = constant

i.e. $\dfrac{p_1 V_1}{T_1} = \dfrac{p_2 V_2}{T_2}$

Units : p_1 = initial pressure
p_2 = final pressure
V_1 = initial volume
V_2 = final volume
T_1 = initial temperature in kelvins
T_2 = final temperature in kelvins

Any convenient units can be used for pressure and volume, provided that p_1 and p_2 have the same units; and V_1 and V_2 have the same units.

(*i*)   0 °C   =   0 + 273 = 273 K
15 °C   =   15 + 273 = 288 K
p_1 = $p_2 = p$
V_1 =   576 cm^3; V_2 = ?

$$\left(\frac{p \times 576}{288}\right) = \frac{p \times V_2}{273} = 746 \text{ cm}^2$$

$$\therefore \quad V_2 = \frac{273}{288} \times 576 = \boxed{546 \text{ cm}^3 \text{ at } °C}$$

$$(ii) \qquad V_2 = 373/288 \times 576 = \boxed{746 \text{ cm}^3}$$

NOTE : If pressure is constant, as in the above example, i.e. $p_1 = p_2$ the formula becomes:

$\dfrac{V_1}{T_1} = \dfrac{V_2}{T_2}$. If volume is constant, i.e. $V_1 = V_2$, then the formula becomes $\dfrac{p_1}{T_1} = \dfrac{p_2}{T^2}$.

CONSERVATION OF ENERGY

Example 35 : A waterfall is 100 m high. If all the potential energy is converted into heat energy, find the difference in temperature between the top and bottom of the fall. (GIVEN : $g = 9.88$ m/s² and specific heat capacity of water $= 4200$ J kg⁻¹ K⁻¹)

Solution : The total potential energy available $= m \, g \, h$

Units : $\quad m = $ mass of water in kg

$\qquad\quad g = 9.81$ m/s²

$\qquad\quad h = $ height of fall in m

Potential energy converted into heat energy $\qquad = m \times 9.8 \times 100$ J $\quad = 980$ mJ

Heat gained by water $\qquad = $ mass $\times$ specific heat capacity $\times$ temperature rise

$\qquad\qquad\qquad\qquad\qquad = m \times 4200 \times t$ J

$m \times 4200 \times t \qquad = 980$ m

Therefore, $t \qquad\qquad\qquad = (980/4200) = \boxed{0.23 \text{ }^\circ\text{C}}$

Example 36 : A lead bullet moving at 70 m s⁻¹ is brought to rest on hitting a target. If 80% of its energy is converted into heat energy, find the rise in temperature (given the specific heat capacity of lead $= 140$ J kg⁻¹ K⁻¹).

Solution : Total kinetic energy of bullet $= \frac{1}{2} \, mv^2$

Units : $\quad m$, mass in kg

$\qquad\qquad v$, velocity in m s⁻¹

Therefore, energy converted into heat energy $= (80/100) \times \frac{1}{2} \times m \times 70^2$ J

Heat gained by bullet $=$ mass $\times$ specific heat capacity $\times$ temperature rise

$\qquad\qquad\qquad\qquad = m \times 140 \times t$

Therefore, $m \times 140 \times t = (80/100) \times \dfrac{m \times 70 \times 70}{2}$

Therefore, $t = 80 \times 70 \times 70/(100 \times 2 \times 140) \quad = 56/4 = \boxed{14 \text{ }^\circ\text{C}}$

LIGHT

There are no difficulties in changing to SI units in problems on reflection, refraction, optical instruments, etc.

PHOTOMETRY

TABLE 4.7

SI UNITS IN LIGHT

Term	Symbol	Unit	Abbreviation
1. Luminous flux	F	lumen	lm
2. Luminous intensity	I	candela	cd
3. Luminance (objective brightness)	L	candela per square metre	cd/m²
4. Illumination	E	lumen per square metre or lux	lx

Example 37 : A street lamp of 800 cd is 8 m above the road.   Find the illumination at a point 6 m from the point vertically beneath the lamp.

Solution :   At C, the light is incident at an angle θ to the normal and $BC = 10$ m from the right-angled triangle ABC (Fig. 4.3).

Illumination $E = \dfrac{I \cos \theta}{BC^2} = 800 \times 8/10 \times 1/10^2$

$$= 64/100 \quad = \quad \boxed{6.4 \text{ lx}}$$

NOTE :   1 lux (lx) = 1 (lm)/m²

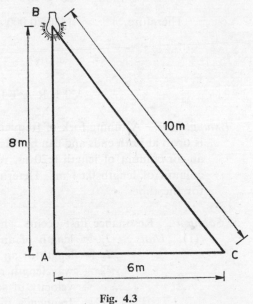

Fig. 4.3

SOUND

Datum : Velocity of sound in air = 340 m s⁻¹, unless otherwise stated.

Example 38 : A thunder clap is heard 4 s after a lightning flash is seen. What is the distance of the storm centre?

Solution : distance $\quad=\quad$ velocity $\times$ time

$$d \quad = \quad 340 \times 4 = \boxed{1360 \text{ m}}$$

Units : velocity in m s^{-1}
time in s

Example 39 : Find the wave-lengths in air and water of sounds of frequency (f) 20 Hz and 20 kHz. (Given velocity of sound in air$=340$ ms^{-1} and velocity of sound in water$=1480$ m s^{-1}).

Solution :

$v = f\lambda$, where f is the frequency and λ the wave length.

(i) $\quad$ at $f = 20$ Hz

(a) *In air :* $\quad 340 = 20\,\lambda$

Therefore, $\lambda = 340/20 = \boxed{17 \text{ m}}$

(b) *In water :* $\quad v = f\lambda$
$$1480 = 20\,\lambda$$

Therefore, $\lambda = 1480/20 = \boxed{74 \text{ m}}$

(ii) $\quad$ at f $\quad = 20$ kHz

(a) *In air:* $\quad v = f\lambda$
$$340 = 20 \times 10^3\,\lambda$$

Therefore, $\lambda = 340/(2 \times 10^4 \text{ m}) = \boxed{0.017 \text{ m}}$

(b) *In water:* $\quad v = f \times \lambda$
$$1480 = 20 \times 10^3 \times \lambda$$

Therefore, $\lambda = 1480/20\,000 = \boxed{0.074 \text{ m}}$

VIBRATING AIR COLUMNS

Example 40 : A tuning fork of frequency 384 Hz is sounded over the end of a long tube which is open at both ends and can be raised or lowered in water.   When the tube is adjusted to give an air-column of length 0.20 m, resonance first occurs.   Resonance next occurs for an air column of length 0.64 m.   Determine the velocity of sound in air and the end-correction for the tube.

Solution : Resonance first occurs when the air column produces its fundamental note.

(1) $\quad$ *Units :* $\quad l_1 =$ length of air column in m (at first resonance)
$\qquad\qquad\quad l_2 =$ length of air column in m (at second resonance)
$\qquad\qquad\quad \lambda_0 =$ wavelength of fundamental note in m
$\qquad\qquad\quad c =$ velocity of sound in m s^{-1} $= 340$ m s^{-1}
$\qquad\qquad\quad f =$ frequency in Hz

If e is the end correction, then

$$(l_1 + e) = \lambda_0/4 \qquad (1)$$
$$(l_2 + e) = (3/4)\,\lambda_0 \qquad (2)$$

Multiply equation (1) by 3, we get

$$3l_1 + 3\,e = (3/4)\,\lambda_0 = l_2 + e$$

or $\quad 2\,e = l_2 - 3\,l_1$ or $e = \dfrac{l_2 - 3\,l_1}{2}$

Since, $\quad l_2 = 0.64$ m and $l_1 = 0.20$ m

$$e = \frac{0.64 - 3 \times 0.20}{2} = (0.04/2) = \boxed{0.02 \text{ m}}$$

Therefore, $\lambda_0 = 4\,(l_1 + 0.02)$

Since $\quad f = 384$ Hz

$$c/384 = 4\,(0.20 + 0.02) \text{ or } c = 384 \times 0.88 = 337.92 \text{ m s}^{-1}$$

Velocity of sound in air $= \boxed{338 \text{ m s}^{-1}}$

TRANSVERSE VIBRATIONS OF STRINGS

Example 41 :   Find the frequency of the fundamental note given by a stretched wire if it is 0.60 m long, has a mass of 10 g and a tension of 960 N.

Solution :   Formula, $f = \dfrac{1}{2\,l}\,\sqrt{\dfrac{T}{m}}$

Units : f = frequency in Hz $\qquad\qquad$ T = tension in N
$\qquad\quad$ l = length in m $\qquad\qquad\qquad$ m = mass of unit length in kg m^{-1}
$\qquad\quad$ $m = 100/6 \times 1/10^3 \quad = 1/60$ kg m^{-1}

$$f = \frac{1}{2 \times 0.60}\,\sqrt{0.60 \times 10^2 \times 960} \qquad \boxed{200 \text{ Hz}}$$

CURRENT ELECTRICITY

Units Commonly Used

CURRENT

1 ampere $= 1$ A
1 milliampere $= 1$ mA $= 1/1000$ A $= 10^{-3}$ A $= 0.001$ A
1 microampere $= 1\,\mu$ A $\quad = 1/1\,000\,000$ A
$\qquad\qquad\qquad\qquad\qquad = 10^{-6}$ A
$\qquad\qquad\qquad\qquad\qquad = 0.000\,001$ A

VOLTAGE	1 volt = 1 V
	1 millivolt = 1 mV = 1/1000 V = 10^{-3} V = 0.001 V
	1 kilovolt = 1 kv = 1000 V = 10^3 V

RESISTANCE	1 ohm = 1 Ω
	1 kilohm = 1 k Ω = 1000 = 10^3 Ω
	1 megohm = 1 MΩ = 1 000 000 = 10^6 Ω

ELECTROLYSIS

Important Data

Symbol for 1 kilogram per coulomb is 1 kg C^{-1} (unit for electrochemical equivalent—ece) (See p. 54). Symbol for 1 coulomb per kilogram is 1 C kg^{-1} (unit for specific charge).

Some Important Electrochemical Equivalents

Copper: 0.000 000 33 kg C^{-1} = 0.33×10^{-6} kg C^{-1}
Hydrogen: 0.000 000 010 5 kg C^{-1} = 0.0105×10^{-6} kg C^{-1}
Nickel: 0.000 000 30 kg C^{-1} = 0.30×10^{-6} kg C^{-1}
Silver: 0.000 001 12 kg C^{-1} = 1.12×10^{-6} kg C^{-1}

Specific Charge

Copper: 3.0×10^6 C kg^{-1}
Hydrogen: 95.2×10^6 C kg^{-1}
Nickel: 3.3×10^6 C kg^{-1}
Silver: 0.893×10^6 C kg^{-1}

Example 63 :   What is the mass of silver that will be deposited in a silver voltameter by the passage of a current of 3 A for 2 hours ?   If a zinc voltameter is in series with the silver voltameter, calculate the mass of zinc deposited, given the chemical equivalents of silver and zinc are 108 and 32.7 respectively.

Solution :   Using electrochemical equivalent formula: $m = zIt$
m = mass deposited in kg $m = 1.12 \times 10^{-6} \times 3 \times 3600$
z = ece in kg C^{-1} $= 24\ 192 \times 10^{-6}$ kg
I = current in A $= 24\ 192 \times 10^{-3}$ g

t = time in s $= \boxed{24.192 \text{ g Ag}}$

Using specific charge $mq = It$
m = mass deposited in kg
q = specific charge in C kg^{-1}

I = current in A

t = time in s

$m = 0.892 \times 10^{-6} = 3 \times 2 \times 3600$

$m = \dfrac{3 \times 2 \times 3600}{0.893 \times 10^6} = \dfrac{21\ 600}{0.893} \times 10^{-6}$ kg $= 24\ 192 \times 10^{-6}$ kg

$= 24\ 192 \times 10^{-3}$ g $= \boxed{24.192 \text{ g Ag}}$

From Faraday's 2nd law of electrolysis:

$$\dfrac{\text{mass of zinc}}{\text{mass of silver}} = \dfrac{\text{electrochemical equivalent of Zn}}{\text{electrochemical equivalent of Ag}}$$

Therefore $m/24.192 = 32.7/108$, where m is the mass of Zinc.

$m = \dfrac{24.192 \times 32.7}{108} = \boxed{7.325 \text{ g Zn}}$

HEATING EFFECT (JOULE'S LAW)

Datum : The specific heat capacity of water = 4200 J kg^{-1} K^{-1}

Example 64 : A 3 kW electric kettle contains 1 kg of water and the heat capacity of the kettle is 300 J K^{-1}. Find the time taken to raise the water to its boiling point if its initial temperature is 30 °C.

Solution : The electric energy supplied in joules = $3000 \times t$ where t is the time taken in seconds.
The energy required to heat the water = mass × specific heat capacity × temperature change
The energy required to heat the vessel = (heat capacity × temperature change)
The electric energy supplied = the total heat energy
Therefore, $3000\ t = 1 \times 4200 \times (100 - 30) + 300 \times (100 - 30)$

$\qquad\qquad 3000\ t = 4200 \times 70 + 300 \times 70$

$\qquad\qquad\qquad = 70\ (4200 + 300) = 70 \times 4500$

$\qquad\qquad 3t\qquad = 7 \times 45$ or $t = 105$ s $= \boxed{1 \text{ min } 45 \text{ s}}$

ENERGY & POWER

Example 65 : An electric heater has two elements each rated at 1 kW. During one week, the heater is used for 28 hours with one element switched on and for another 20 hours with both elements swtiched on. The cost of the first 60 units is 40 paise per kW h and the remaining units are charged at 20 paise per kW h. Find the total cost.

Solution : During one week, one electric heater of 1 kW load is used for 28 h. Therefore, its load is 28 kW h.

For 20 hours, load is $(1+1)$ kW $\times$ 20 h $= 40$ kW h

$$\text{Total energy consumed} = \boxed{68 \text{ kW h}}$$

Out of this, for 60 kW h, the cost of energy $= 60 \times 40/100 = $ Rs. 24
For the balance 8 kW h, the cost of energy $= 8 \times 20/100 = $ Rs. 1.60

Total cost $=$ Rs 24 $+$ Rs. 1.60 $= \boxed{\text{Rs. 25.60}}$

4.12 SI Units in Chemistry

Atomic Weight

The atomic weight of an element is a number which is the average of the masses of its various isotopes, weighted accorded to their relative abundance, on a scale in which the 12C nuclide of carbon is given the value of 12 (exact). For example, on this scale, 35.543 is the atomic weight of chlorine, since this is the average of the masses of the various isotopes having regard to their relative percentage occurrence.

Formula Weight

The formula weight of a chemical entity (atom, radical, molecule, ion, etc.) is the sum of the atomic weights of its constituents. Thus, since, under ordinary conditions, an oxygen molecule consists of two oxygen atoms (atomic weight of oxygen $= 2 \times 15.999\ 4 = 31.998\ 8$; sulphuric acid, whose formula is H_2SO_4, has a formula weight: 98.063 59).

A mass of chemical entity numerically equal in terms of its weight in a certain unit to its formula weight, is termed a 'kilogram-formula weight' or 'gram-formula weight' etc., according to the mass-units employed. Thus, 31.998 8 kg, 31.998 8 g, are respectively the kilogram- and gram-formula weights of oxygen.

Valency

The valency of an atom or radical (i.e. a group of atoms) is the number of hydrogen atoms with which it will react chemically. Valency is always an integer (1, 2, 3 etc.), but for a given atom or radical it can have different values in respect of different chemical reactions.

Equivalent Weights

The equivalent weight of a substance is the quotient of its formula-weight divided by its valency, i.e.

$$\text{equivalent weight (in kg)} = \frac{\text{formula weight (kg)}}{\text{valency}}$$

Electrochemical Equivalent

The electro-chemical equivalent of a substance is the mass of it liberated during electrolysis by the passage of unit quantity of electricity, i.e. by unit current of one ampere for unit time of one second. The SI unit for electrochemical equivalent is 'kilogram-per-coulomb' (kg C^{-1}).

The Faraday

The quantity of electricity, which liberates one gram-equivalent weight of a substance has been measured and found to be 96 487.0 coulombs.

This quantity of electricity is termed the 'faraday' or 'faraday constant'. *Symbol*: F; *Unit*: $C\,kg^{-1}$.

Value of F in SI $= 9.648\ 70 \times 10^4\ C\ mol^{-1}$

Avogadro's Constant

If M is the mass of a molecule expressed on the atomic weight scale and m kg its mass on the kg scale, then,

$$M = km,$$

where k is the constant factor which converts masses on one scale to the other. The number of molecules of a substance contained in one kilogram formula weight is M/m and, from the above equation, this is constant and independent of the substance. Thus, the kilogram formula weights of all substances contain the same number of molecules. A similar statement can be made about the gram formula weights of substances. The number of molecules in one gram-formula weight of any substance is called Avogadro's constant

Symbol: L or N_A.   *Unit*: mol^{-1}

Value of N_A in SI $= 6.022\ 52 \times 10^{23}\ mol^{-1}$

Important Chemical Data in SI

Table 4.8 summarises the important data in

SI units for (*i*) atomic weight, (*ii*) valency and (*iii*) electrochemical equivalent (ece) for some metals and radicals.

CHARACTERISTIC EQUATION OF A PERFECT GAS

$PV = RT$ is called the characteristic gas equation in which R is called the 'Characteristic Gas Gas Constant' or merely *'Gas Constant'*.

Units of R *in SI*:   Joules/kgK

Value of R (Molar Gas Constant)
$= 8.314\ 3 \times J\ mol^{-1}\ K^{-1}$

Boltzmann Constant: Symbol: k

$$\text{The ratio} = \frac{R\ (\text{Universal Gas Constant})}{N\ (\text{Avogadro's number})}$$

$$= \text{Boltzmann constant } (k)$$

$$k = \frac{8.314\ 3\ J\ mol^{-1}\ K^{-1}}{6.022\ 52\ 10^{23}\ mols^{-1}}$$

$$= 1.380\ 54 \times 10^{-23}\ JK^{-1}$$

TABLE 4.8

IMPORTANT CHEMICAL DATA

Atom or radical	Chemical symbol	Atomic weight or Formula weight (kg)	Valency (number)	Electrochemical Equivalent (kg/C)
Aluminium	Al	26.981 5	3	9.321×10^{-8}
Chlorine	Cl	35.453	1	36.744×10^{-8}
Copper	Cu	63.54	2	32.927×10^{-2}
Hydrogen	H	1.007 97	1	1.045×10^{-8}
Hydroxyl	OH	17.007 4	1	1.626×10^{-8}
Nickel	Ni	58.71	2	30.429×10^{-8}
Nitrate	NO_3	62.004 9	1	64.262×10^{-8}
Oxygen	O	15.999 4	2	8.291×10^{-8}
Silver	Ag	107.870	1	111.797×10^{-8}
Sulphate	SO_4	96.062	2	49.780×10^{-8}
Zinc	Zn	65.37	2	33.880×10^{-8}

4.13 SI Units in Geography

The SI units required in Geography are:

(1) Unit of *length* for expressing heights of mountains or depths of oceans: metres or preferably km.

(2) Units for expressing *rainfall:* mm *instead of* inches.

(3) Units for areas of land, lakes etc: square metres (m^2) *or*
are $= 10^2$ m^2 *or* hectares $= 10^4$ m^2

(4) Unit of *Volume* : cubic metres (m^3) *or for small volumes*: litres (l) 1 litre$= dm^3 = 10^{-3}$ m^3

(5) Unit of *temperature* : degrees celsius (°C)

(6) Unit of *wind pressure*: N/m^2 or bars or millibars (m bar)
(1 bar$=10^5$ N/m^2 and 1 m bar$=10$ N/m^2)

4.14 SI Units in Technical Subjects (at pre-university levels)

All the required units like length, area, volume, mass, weight, force, power and energy have been already dealt with.

4.15 SI Units in Domestic Science

All the required units have already been covered under mathematics, physics and chemistry.

CHAPTER FIVE

SI Units in Engineering and Science

5.1 Introduction

The use of SI units in engineering and science is explained in this chapter by means of worked examples.

5.2 SI Units in Physics

SI units that figure in the problems are given in Tables 5.1 and 5.2.

MECHANICAL ENERGY

1. *Potential energy* mgh joules
2. *Kinetic energy* $\frac{1}{2} mv^2$ joules
3. *Pressure energy*   If a body of fluid has a mass m, pressure of p and a density of ρ, it has an energy $= mp/\rho$ joules

   In these three equations, it is necessary to work in the coherent system of SI units, i.e.

m *in* kg	v *in* m/s
g *in* m/s^2	p *in* N/m^2
h *in* m	ρ *in* kg/m^3

NOTE: Each of the energy formulae gives values in joules (J) only.

TABLE 5.1

SI UNITS AND THEIR CGS EQUIVALENTS

Quantity and its nature	SI unit	Symbol	cgs unit
Force (vector)	newton	N	dyne
Mass (scalar)	kilogram	kg	gram
Momentum (vector)	newton second	N s	dyne second
Energy (scalar)	joule	J	erg
Power (scalar)	watt	W	erg s^{-1}

NOTE

Force = rate of change of momentum
$$= \frac{\text{mass} \times \text{velocity}}{\text{time}}$$
= mass × acceleration

Torque = rate of change of angular momentum
$$= I \times \frac{\text{angular velocity}}{\text{time}}$$
$= I \times$ angular acceleration

where I is the mass moment of inertia.

Conservation of momentum: The *linear momentum* of a system on which no external forces act is *constant*. The *angular momentum* of a system on which no external torque acts is *constant*.

57

SI UNITS FOR DYNAMICS

TABLE 5.2

LINEAR AND CIRCULAR MOTION

Quantity	Symbol	Abbreviation of unit
Linear motion		
Displacement	s	m
Mass	m	kg
Time	t	s
Velocity (ds/dt)	v	m s^{-1}
Momentum (mv)	—	kg m s^{-1}
Acceleration (dv/dt)	a	m s^{-2}
Force (ma)	F	N
Energy (Fs)	E	J
Kinetic energy ($\frac{1}{2} mv^2$)	—	J
Period of a simple pendulum $\left(T = 2\pi \sqrt{\dfrac{l}{g}} \right)$	T	s
Circular motion		
Angular displacement	θ	rad
Moment of inertia	I	kg m^2
Time	t	s
Angular velocity $\left(\dfrac{d\theta}{dt} \right)$		rad s^{-1}
Angular momentum	$I\omega$	kg m^2/s
Angular acceleration $\left(\dfrac{d^2\theta}{dt^2} \right)$		rad/s^2
Kinetic or rotational energy ($\frac{1}{2} I\omega^2$)	—	J

NOTE : Centripetal and centrifugal forces are equal in magnitude and act in opposite directions.

One revolution (or 1 cycle) $= 2\pi$ rad

Frequency, $f = \dfrac{\omega}{2\pi}$ Hz

Periodic time for 1 revolution, $T = \dfrac{2\pi}{\omega}$ Hz^{-1}

RELATIONS BETWEEN LINEAR AND CIRCULAR QUANTITIES

Some useful relations between linear and circular quantities are summarized below:

If v be the instantaneous tangential velocity of a mass m, rotating about an axis at a radius r, then:

angular velocity, $\quad \omega = \dfrac{v}{r}$ rad/s

centripetal acceleration $= \omega^2 r = \dfrac{v^2}{r}$ m/s^2

centripetal force $\Big\}$
centrifugal force $\Big\}$ $\quad F = m\omega^2 r = \dfrac{mv^2}{r}$ N

MOMENTS OF INTERTIA OF BODIES

The following notes on moments of inertia of bodies will be useful in working out problems:

If $M = $ mass, $r = $ radius of the body

1. for a thin ring or thin-walled tube rotating about its axis:
$$I = Mr^2 \text{ kg m}^2$$

2. for a disc or solid cylinder rotating about its axis:
$$I = \tfrac{1}{2} Mr^2 \text{ kg m}^2$$

3. for a solid sphere rotating about a diameter:
$$I = \frac{2}{5} Mr^2 \text{ kg m}^2$$

4. for a uniform rod of length r rotating about one end:
$$I = \frac{1}{3} Mr^2 \text{ kg m}^2$$

Units for I: kg m^2

All other cases can be derived from the above by the use of the theorems of parallel and perpendicular axes given below:

Theorem of Parallel Axes: If a body of mass M has a moment of inertia I_0 about an axis through its centre of gravity, then its moment of inertia about a parallel axis at distance h from the first is:
$$I = I_0 + Mh^2 \text{ kg m}^2$$

Theorem of Perpendicular Axes: If a plane lamina has a moment of inertia I_z about an axis perpendicular to its plane and moments of inertia I_y and I_x about mutually perpendicular axes in the plane of the lamina:
$$I_z = I_y + I_x \text{ kg m}^2$$

KINETIC ENERGY & POTENTIAL ENERGY

Example 1: What is the energy possessed by a 6000 kg aeroplane while flying at 13.5 m s^{-1} at an altitude of 600 m? Use $g = 9.81$ m s^{-2}.

Solution:

Mass of aeroplane	$= 6000$ kg
Potential energy (P E)	$= mgh$ joules
	$= 6000 \times 9.81 \times 600$ J $\quad = 3533 \times 10^4$ J
Velocity	$= 13.5$ m s^{-1}
Kinetic energy (K E)	$= \frac{1}{2} mv^2$ joules
	$= \frac{1}{2} \times 6000 \times 13.5^2 \quad = 54.67 \times 10^4$ J
Total energy	$= P E + K E$
	$= (3533 + 54.67) \times 10^4$ J $\quad = \boxed{588 \times 10^4 \text{ J}}$

POWER CALCULATIONS ON A MOTOR CAR

Example 2: A motor car is running on a level road at a uniform rate of 96.6 km/h (60 mph). If the frictional resistance offered by air and road to the motor car is 222.5 newtons (50 lb wt), calculate the power in kW developed by the engine of the car.

Solution:

96.6 km/h	$= 26.82$ m/s
Force exerted by the engine	$= 222.5$ N
Distance moved by car in one second	$= 26.82$ m

$\therefore$ work done by engine in 1 second $= 222.5 \times 26.82 \dfrac{\text{N m}}{\text{s}}$ (or J/s)

$$= 5967 \text{ W} = 5.967 \text{ kW} = \boxed{6 \text{ kW}}$$

RATE OF WORKING OF A STEAM ENGINE

Example 3: A steam engine cylinder is 0.38 m (15 in) diameter. The mean pressure during a stroke is 344 800 N/m^2 (50 lb/in^2) and the length of the stroke is 0.56 m (22 in). Find the work done in one stroke and if it does 70 strokes per minute, express the power in kW.

Solution:

Thrust on piston (in newtons) $=$ pressure $\times$ area

$$= \left(344\,800 \times \frac{22}{7} \times \frac{0.38}{2} \times \frac{0.38}{2} \right) \text{ N}$$

In one stroke, this force moves through a distance of 0.56 m.

Work done in one stroke $=$ thrust $\times$ distance

$$= 344\,800 \times \frac{22}{7} \times \frac{0.38}{2} \times \frac{0.38}{2} \times 0.56 \text{ J}$$

$$= \boxed{21\,900 \text{ J}}$$

Work done/second $= \dfrac{21900 \times 70}{60} = 25550$ W $\quad = \boxed{25.55 \text{ kW}}$

STEAM ENGINE GOVERNOR

Example 4: A pair of conical governor balls, each of mass 11 kg is rotating at 42 rev/min. Find the tension in each tie rod which is one metre long.

Solution: 1 complete revolution $= 2\pi$ radians

$\therefore$ 42 revs/minute $= 42 \times 2\pi$ rad/min

$\therefore \quad \omega \qquad\qquad = 42 \times 2 \times \dfrac{22}{7} \times \dfrac{1}{60}$ rad/second

$\qquad\qquad\qquad = \dfrac{22}{5}$ rad/s

Tension in each tie rod $\qquad = m\,\omega^2\,l$

$\qquad\qquad\qquad\qquad\quad = 11 \times \dfrac{22}{5} \times \dfrac{22}{5} \times 1$ newtons

$\qquad\qquad\qquad\qquad\quad = \boxed{213\ N}$

SIMPLE PENDULUM

Example 5:   Find the length of a seconds pendulum, taking $g = 9.81$ m/s^2.

Solution: A seconds pendulum is one that beats seconds, i.e. it has a period of oscillation of of 2 seconds.

Hence $\quad 2 = 2\pi \sqrt{\dfrac{l}{9.81}}$

or $\qquad 4 = 4\pi^2\, l/9.81$

or $\qquad l = \dfrac{4 \times 9.81}{4 \times \pi^2} = 0.9940$ m $= \boxed{99.4\ cm}$

FORCE AND MOMENTUM CHANGE

Example 6:   A hose pipe ejects water at a speed of 0.2 m/s through a hole of area 100 cm^2. If the water strikes a wall normally, calculate the force (in newtons) on the wall. Assume that after the collision the velocity of the water normal to the wall is zero.

Solution: 100 cm^2 $= 100 \times 10^{-4}$ m^2

Volume of water striking the wall per second $\qquad = 100 \times 10^{-4} \times 0.2 = 0.002$ m^3

$\therefore$ Mass per second striking wall $\qquad\qquad = 0.002 \times 10^3$ kg/s $= 2$ kg/s

Velocity change of water on striking the wall $\quad = 0.2 - 0 = 0.2$ m/s

$\therefore$ Change of momentum per second $\qquad\quad = 2$ (kg/s) $\times 0.2$ (m/s)

$\qquad\qquad\qquad\qquad\qquad\qquad\qquad\quad = 2 \times 0.2 \times \dfrac{kg \times m}{s^2} = \boxed{0.4\ N}$

MASS-ENERGY CONVERSION

Example 7:   Einstein showed that, in a nuclear reaction, when a mass of Δm kg is lost, there is a release of ΔE joules of energy.   His equation is:

$$\Delta E \qquad = \qquad \Delta mc^2$$

where c =   velocity of light = 3×10^8 m/s

Calculate the energy released in a nuclear reaction when a milligram mass of matter is converted to energy.

Solution: $m = 1$ mg $= 10^{-3}$ g $= 10^{-6}$ kg

$E = mc^2 = 10^{-6} \times (3 \times 10^8)^2$

$$= \boxed{9 \times 10^{10} \text{ J}}$$

NOTE: (*i*)   This energy will light about 250 000 numbers of 100 W electric lamps for about an hour. The problem gives an idea of the enormous amount of energy that is released when a small amount of matter (mass) is expended in a nuclear reaction.

(*ii*)   Significant mass changes occur only in nuclear reactions.

MOTION IN A CIRCLE (CENTRIFUGE)

Example 8:   A pendulum bob of mass 1 kg is attached to a string 1 m long and made to revolve in a horizontal circle of radius 0.6 m.   Find the tension of the string and the period of the motion.

Solution: Let M be the bob and OM the string (Fig. 5.1). If T be the tension of the string in newtons, and θ the angle of inclination of OM to the horizontal, then, for motion in a cirlcle of radius $r = 0.6$ m,

$$T \cos \theta = \frac{mv^2}{r} = \frac{mv^2}{0.6} \qquad (1)$$

Since the bob does not move in a vertical direction, $T \sin\theta = mg$

$\text{Cos } \theta = \dfrac{60}{100} = \dfrac{3}{5}.$ Hence sin $\theta = \dfrac{4}{5}$

$\therefore \quad T = \dfrac{mg}{\sin \theta} = \dfrac{1 \times 9.81}{4/5} = \boxed{12.26 \text{ N}}$

$v = \dfrac{0.6 \, T \cos \theta}{m} = \dfrac{0.6 \times 12.25 \times 3}{1 \times 5}$

$= 2.1$ m/s

$\dfrac{v}{r} = \omega = \dfrac{2.1}{0.6} = 3.5$ m/sec^2

Period $= \dfrac{2 \pi}{3.5} = \dfrac{88}{49} \approx \boxed{1.8 \text{ sec}}$

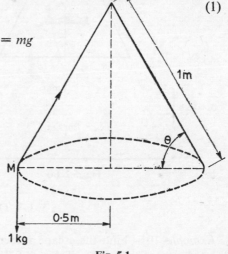

Fig. 5.1

WEIGHTLESSNESS

Example 9

In Chapter 4, we drew a distinction between mass and weight and discussed the concept of weightlessness in space travel. This will now be explained with a numerical example.

When a rocket is fired to launch a space craft and astronaut into an orbit around the earth, the initial acceleration is very high owing to the large initial thrust required. This acceleration (α) is about 15 g, where $g=9.81$, the acceleration due to gravity at the earth's surface.

Let R be the reaction of the couch to which the astronaut is initially strapped. Then, from the equation $F = ma$ we get $R - mg = ma = m \times 15\,g$, where m is the mass of the astronaut. This gives $R = 16\,g$. This reaction force is 16 times the weight of the astronaut and thus, to start with, he experiences a very large force to withstand for which he receives special conditioning and training. While in the orbit, let the acceleration of the spacecraft and the astronaut be g' (in magnitude), where g' is the acceleration due to gravity outside the satellite at the particular height of the orbit. If R' is the reaction of the surface of the satellite in contact with the astronaut, then, for circular motion, $F = mg' - R' = ma = mg'$. Thus, R' becomes zero. Consequently, the astronaut becomes weightless and he experiences no reaction from the floor when he walks about. On the surface of the earth, we feel the reaction of the ground and are thus concious of our weight. Inside an elevator which is coming down fast, the reaction at our feet diminishes. If the lift falls freely, the acceleration of objects inside is the same as that outside and hence the reaction on them is zero. This causes the sensation of 'weightlessness'. In orbit, objects inside a spacecraft are also in a state of 'free fall' because they have the same acceleration g' as the space craft itself. Hence, the sensation of weightlessness.

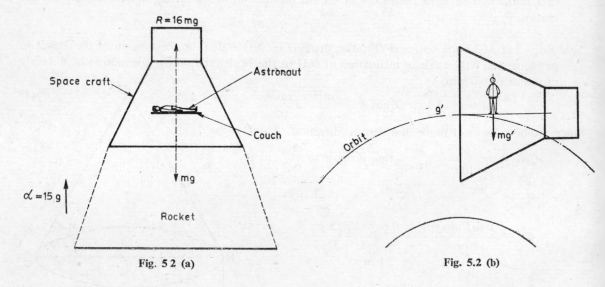

Fig. 5 2 (a)   Fig. 5.2 (b)

VELOCITY OF ESCAPE

Example 10: Find the escape velocity for a rocket to escape completely from the gravitational attraction of the earth. Take $g=9.81$ m/s^2 and the radius of the earth H, $r = 6.4 \times 10^6$ m.

Solution: Suppose a rocket of mass m is fired from the earth's surface P so that it just escapes from the gravitational influence of the earth.

Work done $= m \times$ potential difference between infinity and P

$$= m \times \frac{GM}{r} \text{ where } GM \text{ is the product of } G, \text{ the gravitational constant and } M, \text{ the mass of the earth}$$

or $v = \sqrt{\dfrac{2GM}{r}}$ where v is called the *escape velocity*.

Now, $\dfrac{GM}{r^2} = g$

$\therefore \quad v = \sqrt{2\,gr}$

$\therefore \quad v = 2 \times 9.81 \times 6.4 \times 10^6$

$\quad = 11 \times 10^3$ m/s $= \boxed{11 \text{ km/s}}$

Note on escape velocities (V_E)

(*i*) With a velocity of about 8 km/s, a satellite can describe a *circular* orbit close to the earth's surface.

(*ii*) With a velocity > 8 km/s but < 11 km/s, a satellite describes an *elliptical* orbit around the earth.

(*iii*) If $v > V_E$ then the orbit is a *hyperbola*.

(*iv*) If $v = V_E$ then the orbit is a *parabola*.

ROTATION OF RIGID BODIES

Moment of Inertia

Example 11: A heavy flywheel of mass 20 kg and radius 20 cm is mounted on a horizontal axle of radius 1 cm and negligible mass compared with the flywheel. Neglecting friction, find: (*i*) angular acceleration if a force of 40 N is applied tangentially to the axle; and (*ii*) the angular velocity of the flywheel after 15 seconds.

Solution: 20 cm = 0.2 m

(*i*) Moment of inertia (I) of a flywheel $= \dfrac{Ma^2}{2} = \dfrac{20 \times 0.2^2}{2} = 0.4$ kg m²

Couple $=$ force $\times$ radius
$= 40$ N $\times 0.01 = 0.4$ N m
$= I \times$ angular acceleration

$\therefore$ angular acceleration $= \dfrac{\text{couple}}{I} = \dfrac{0.4}{0.4} = \boxed{1 \text{ rad/s}^2}$

(*ii*) After 15 seconds, angular velocity $=$ angular acceleration $\times$ time
$= 1 \times 15 = \boxed{15 \text{ rad/s}}$

Example 12: Calculate the kinetic energy and momentum of a flywheel with the following dimensions when travelling at a velocity of 5 m/s.

Mass of rim $= 1$ kg;   radius $= 0.5$ m;   No. of spokes $= 30$;   mass of spokes $= 0.1$ kg each.

Solution

(*a*) Rim (as a ring): $I = mr^2 = 1 \times (0.5)^2 = 0.25$ kg m^2

(*b*) Spoke (as a rod): $I = \dfrac{1}{3} mr^2 \dfrac{1}{3} \times 0.1 \times (0.5)^2 = \dfrac{1}{3} \times 0.025$ kg m^2

∴ Total $I = 0.25 + \left(30 \times \dfrac{1}{3} \times 0.025 \right) = 0.50$ kg m^2

Total mass $= 1 + (30 \times 0.1) = 4.0$ kg

$$KE = \tfrac{1}{2} mv^2 + \tfrac{1}{2} I \omega^2 \text{ (where } \omega = \frac{v}{r}\text{rad/s)}$$

$$= (\tfrac{1}{2} \times 4 \times 25) + \tfrac{1}{2} \times 0.5 \times \left(\frac{25}{0.25} \right) = 50 + 25 = \boxed{75 \text{ J}}$$

Linear momentum $=$ mass $\times$ velocity $= (4.0 \times 5.0) = \boxed{20 \text{ kg m/s}}$

Angular momentum $= I \times \omega = 0.5 \times \left(\dfrac{5}{0.5} \right) = \boxed{5.0 \text{ kg m}^2/\text{s}}$

NOTE: The linear and circular momenta, unlike energies, should not be added together because their respective units are not the same.

Angular Acceleration

Example 13: A wheel starting from rest attains a speed of 2400 rev/min in 10 seconds.   Find (*i*) its angular acceleration   (*ii*) the number of revolutions made before attaining full speed.

Solution

(*i*) *Data:* $\omega_1 = 0$; $\omega_2 = \dfrac{2400}{60} 40 = \text{rev/s} = 40 \times 2 \pi = 80 \pi$ rad/s

$$\therefore \alpha = \frac{80 \times 22}{7 \times 10} = \frac{176}{7} = \boxed{25.13 \text{ rad/s}^2}$$

(*ii*) In order to find the angle swept out, use the formula:

$\theta = \omega_1 t + \tfrac{1}{2} \alpha t^2$, where $\omega_1 =$ initial angular velocity.

$\therefore \theta = 0 + \tfrac{1}{2} \times 25.13 \times 10^2 = 1257$ rad $= \boxed{200 \text{ revs}}$ ($\because$ 1 rev $= 2 \pi$ rad)

Example 14: The flywheel of a car engine is slowed down from 3000 rev/s to 2000 rev/s in 2 seconds. Calculate (*i*) the angular acceleration and (ii) the number of revolutions made by the wheel during the slowing-down period.

Solution

(*i*) $3000 \text{ rev/min} = \dfrac{3000}{60} \text{ rev/s} = 50 \times 2\pi \text{ rad/s} = 100\pi \text{ rad/s}$

$2000 \text{ rev/min} = \dfrac{2000}{60} \text{ rev/s} = 2\pi \times \dfrac{200}{6} \text{ rad/s}$

$t = 2 \text{ s}$

$\omega_2 = \omega_1 + \alpha t$

$\dfrac{200}{3}\pi = 100\pi + 2\alpha$

$\therefore \quad \alpha = \dfrac{\pi}{2}\left(\dfrac{200}{3} - 100\right) = -\pi\left(\dfrac{100}{6}\right) \text{ rad/s}^2 = \boxed{-52.3 \text{ rad/s}^2}$

(*ii*) $\theta = \omega_1 t + \tfrac{1}{2}\alpha t^2$

Hence $\theta = 100\pi \times 2 + \tfrac{1}{2}(-52.3) \times 2^2$

$= 200\pi - 104.6 = 524 \text{ rad} = \boxed{83.3 \text{ rev}}$

$(\because \quad 1 \text{ rev} = 2 \text{ rad})$

RULE: To convert rev/min to rad/sec, multiply by $\pi/30$.

Angular Acceleration

Example 15: A motor car travelling around a circular track of 100 m radius accelerates uniformly from a speed of 15 m/s to 35 m/s in 7.5 s. Find its angular acceleration.

Solution

$\alpha t = \text{tangential acceleration} = \dfrac{35 - 15}{7.5} \text{ m/s}^2 = \dfrac{20}{7.5} = 2.67 \text{ m/s}^2$

Since $r = 100 \text{ m}$ $\dfrac{\alpha t}{r} = \dfrac{2.67}{100} = \boxed{0.0267 \text{ rad/s}^2}$

Centripetal Acceleration

Example 16: A motor car is travelling at a constant speed of 72 km/h around a circular path of radius 150 m. Find the centripetal acceleration.

Solution: $v = 75 \text{ km/h} = 20 \text{ m/s}, \quad r = 150 \text{ m}$

Centripetal acceleration $= \dfrac{v^2}{r} = \dfrac{20 \times 20}{150} = \dfrac{8}{3} = \boxed{2.6 \text{ m/s}^2}$

Radial Acceleration

Example 17:   An electron is travelling in a circular orbit of 0.8 m radius in a betatron (a particle accelerator) at a speed of 2.9 × 10⁸ m/s.   Find its radial acceleration.

Solution

$$\text{Radial acceleration } = \frac{(2.9 \times 10^8)^2}{0.8} = \boxed{\begin{array}{l} 10.5 \times 10^{16} \text{ m/s}^2 \\ \text{towards the centre} \end{array}}$$

CENTRIFUGAL FORCE AND BANKING OF RAILWAY TRACK

Example 18:   A railway track curves in an arc of a circle of radius 0.25 km (*r*) and the distance between the two rails is 2 m.   For a maximum speed of 32 km/h (*v*), how much higher should the outer rail be raised over the inner?   Take *g* = 9.81 ms⁻².

Solution: $\tan \theta = \dfrac{v^2}{rg}$

$$v = 32 \text{ km/h} = \frac{32 \times 10^3}{60 \times 60} \text{ m/s}$$

$$\therefore \quad \tan \theta = \frac{32 \times 32 \times 10^6}{0.25 \times 10^3 \times 9.81 \times (3600)^2} = 0.0320$$

$\therefore \quad \theta = 1° \; 50'$ (since θ is small, we can take $\sin \theta = \tan \theta$)

$\therefore \quad \theta = \dfrac{h}{2}$ or $h = 0.063\,88$ m $= \boxed{64 \text{ mm}}$

ENERGY OF FLUIDS

Example 19:   A mass of fluid of 4 kg is located at 5 m above a certain datum.   The fluid has a velocity of 12 m/s, a pressure of 10⁶ N/m² and a density of 10³ kg/m³.   Find the total energy of the fluid with reference to the datum height and zero pressure.

Solution

Total energy   = potential energy + kinetic energy + pressure energy

(1)   potential energy $= mgh = 4 \times 9.81 \times 5 \dfrac{\text{kg} \times \text{m} \times \text{m}}{\text{s}^2}$

$$= \frac{196.2 \text{ kg m}^2}{\text{s}^2} = 196.2 \text{ J} \tag{1}$$

(2)   kinetic energy $= \frac{1}{2} mv^2 = \dfrac{4 \times 144}{2} \text{ kg } \dfrac{\text{m}^2}{\text{s}^2}$

$$= 288 \text{ kg } \frac{\text{m}}{\text{s}^2} = 288 \text{ J} \tag{2}$$

(3)   pressure energy $= \dfrac{mp}{\rho} = \dfrac{4 \times 10^6}{10^3}$ kg $\dfrac{N}{m^2} \dfrac{m^3}{kg}$

$$= 4000 \text{ N m} = 4000 \text{ J} \qquad (3)$$

∴   Total energy = potential energy + kinetic energy + pressure energy

$$= (196.2 + 288 + 4000) \text{ J} = 4484.2 \text{ J}$$

Thus, the total energy of the fluid = $\boxed{4484.2 \text{ J}}$

SURFACE TENSION

The unit of surface tension in SI is N/m. It is determined in the laboratory for various liquids by different methods. The most popular method is the capitallary tube method.

NOTATION

γ = magnitude of surface tension which is the force per unit length acting in the surface of the liquid.

$2 \pi r$ = length of liquid in contact with the glass, where r = radius of the capillary tube

NOTE: γ is in N/m and r in metres

ρ is in kg m^{-3}, h in metres, $g = 9.81$ m s^{-2}

h = length of tube, ρ = density of liquid

Example 20:   In an experiment, the radius r of the capillary tube used is 0.2 mm. The height h of water is 6.6 cm. Assuming the density ρ of the water to be 1000 kg m^{-3}, find the surface tension.

Solution: Let γ be the surface tension.

Hence, $\gamma \times 2 \pi r = \pi r^2 h \rho g$

or $\gamma = \dfrac{hr \rho g}{2}$

$$= \dfrac{6.6 \times 10^{-2} \times 0.2 \times 10^{-3} \times 1000 \times 9.8}{2} = \boxed{6.4 \times 10^{-2} \text{ N/m}}$$

VISCOSITY

There are two kinds of viscosity: (*i*) dynamic viscosity, (*ii*) kinematic viscosity. In SI units, the unit of dynamic viscosity is N s m^{-2} and the unit of kinematic viscosity is m^2 s^{-1}. Being somewhat complicated expressions, they are derived below.

(*i*) *Dynamic viscosity* (η)

By definition, η $= \dfrac{\text{mass}}{\text{length} \times \text{time}}$

In SI, it becomes η $= \dfrac{\text{kg}}{\text{m} \times \text{s}}$

but $N = \dfrac{kg\ m}{s^2}$ or $kg = \dfrac{N\ s^2}{m}$

substituting this value for kg in expression for η, we get,

$$\eta = \frac{N\ s^2}{m^2 \times s} = \frac{N\ s}{m^2}\ \left(\ i.e.\ \frac{newton\ second}{metre\ squared}\ \right)$$

(ii) Kinematic viscosity

$$Kinematic\ viscosity = \frac{dynamic\ viscosity}{density}$$

$$SI\ unit\ for\ dynamic\ viscosity = \frac{N\ s}{m^2}$$

$$SI\ unit\ for\ density\ is\ \frac{kg}{m^3}$$

$\therefore$ SI unit for kinematic viscosity is $\dfrac{Ns}{m^2} \div \dfrac{kg}{m^3}$

$$= \frac{N\ s\ m}{kg}\ \left(\ but\ N = \frac{kg\ m}{s^2}\ \right)$$

$$= \frac{kg\ m^2\ s}{kg\ s^2} = \frac{m^2}{s}$$

NOTES

1. Formerly there were two units in use for absolute or dynamic viscosity. These were the poise (P) and the centipoise (cP).

     1 poise (P) $= 10^{-1}$ N s/m^2
     1 centipoise (cP) $= 10^{-3}$ N s/m^2

2. Formerly, there were two units in use for kinematic viscosity. These were the stoke (St) and the centisiokes (cSt)

     1 stoke (St) $= 10^{-4}$ m^2/s
     1 centistoke (cSt) $= 10^{-6}$ m^2/s

ELASTICITY

Problems in the field of elasticity will involve the three elastic moduli E, G and K and Poisson's ratio ν. Their definitions and the type of problems in which they will occur are summarized in Table 5.3. The modulus of elasticity and the ultimate strength of some materials frequently used in engineering applications are given in Table 5.4. In Tables 5.5 and 5.6, the values of the Modulus of Rigidity and the Bulk Modulus of commonly used materials are given.

The value of E is best expressed in G N/mm^2. The ultimate strength of materials is most conveniently expressed in M N/mm^2 (see Table 5.4).

G, the shear modulus, is expressed N/m^2 for four typical metals in Table 5.5.

Poisson's ratio: As this is a ratio and hence a pure number, its value does not change with the system of units. Its value lies between 0.23 for cast steel and 0.44 for gold and lead.

TABLE 5.3

ELASTIC CONSTANTS

Elastic constant Symbol SI unit	Young's modulus E N/m²	Modulus of rigidity G N/m²	Bulk modulus K N/m²
Definition	$\dfrac{\text{stress}}{\text{strain}}$	$\dfrac{\text{shear stress}}{\text{shear strain}}$	$\dfrac{\text{pressure change}}{\text{volumetric strain}}$
Relates to	change in *length* (tensile)	change in *shape* (shear)	change in *volume* (bulk)
Expression	$E = \dfrac{F/A}{e/l}$	$G = \dfrac{F/A}{\gamma}$	$K = \dfrac{\Delta p}{-\left(\dfrac{\Delta V}{V}\right)}$
Applies to	only solids	solids and liquids	all materials but low value for gases
Occurs in problems relating to	stretching of wires, bending of beams, linear expansion and contraction with temperature	torsion of solids, helical springs	velocity of sound formula for all materials. In a gas, $K=p$ (isothermal) or γp (adiabatic)

TABLE 5.4

YOUNG'S MODULUS AND
ULTIMATE STRENGTH

	E in GN/m²	Ultimate strength (M N/m²)
Aluminium	70	90
Copper, pure	107–130	200–350
Brass	100	350–510
Phospor bronze	120	450–700
Iron, pure	200	290–450
Wrought iron	210	330
Cast iron	100–130	210
Mild steel	210	490
Lead	16	12–17
Magnesium	45	60–190
Silver	83	290

TABLE 5.5

SHEAR MODULUS

	G in N/m²		G in N/m²
Aluminium	0.24×10^{11}	Brass	0.35×10^{11}
Copper	0.4×10^{11}	Lead	0.05×10^{11}

TABLE 5.6

BULK MODULUS

	K in N/m²		K in N/m²
Aluminium	0.7×10^{11}	Cast Iron	0.96×10^{11}
Brass	0.61×10^{11}	Wrought Iron	1.5×10^{11}
Copper	1.2×10^{11}	Steel	1.6×10^{11}
Air		Lead	0.08×10^{11}
(*isothermal*) 10^5		(*adiabatic*)	1.4×10^5

Relation between elastic constants for solids

$$G = \frac{E}{2(1 + v)} \; ; \quad K = \frac{E}{3(1-2\,v)}$$

Example 21: How much will a 30-metre steel tape, 1 cm wide and 0.05 cm thick stretch under a pull of a force of 300 newton, if E, Young's modulus for steel, is 2.0×10^{11} N/m².

Solution: Area of steel tape $= 1 \times 0.05 = 0.05$ cm²

Stress intensity, $p = \dfrac{P}{A} = \dfrac{300}{0.05} = 6000$ N/cm² $= 6000 \times 10^4$ N/m²

$$E = \frac{\text{stress intensity}}{\text{unit strain}}$$

$$e = \frac{p}{E} = \frac{6000 \times 10^4}{2.0 \times 10^{11}}$$

$\therefore$ Total elongation $= \dfrac{6000 \times 10^4}{2 \times 10^{11}} \times 30 \times 100 = \boxed{0.9 \text{ cm}}$

Example 22: A mild steel rod 20 cm long between gauge points and 4 cm in diameter has an axial tensile load of 250 000 N acting on it. The gauge length is extended by 0.2 mm and the diameter reduced to 3.75 cm. Find the stress, strain, modulus of elasticity, the percentage elongation and the percentage reduction in area.

Solution:

Stress intensity $(p) = \dfrac{P}{A} = \dfrac{250\,000}{\dfrac{\pi}{4} \times 4^2} = 19\,000$ N/cm² $= \boxed{19\,000 \times 10^4 \text{ N/m}^2}$

Strain $(e) = \dfrac{0.02}{20} = \boxed{0.001}$

Modulus of Elasticity $(E) = \dfrac{p}{e} = \dfrac{19\,900 \times 10^4}{0.001} = \boxed{1.99 \times 10^{11} \text{ N/m}^2}$

Percentage elongation $= \dfrac{\text{change in length}}{\text{original length}} \times 100 = \dfrac{0.02}{20} \times 100 = \boxed{0.1\%}$

Percentage reduction in area $= \dfrac{\text{decrease in area}}{\text{original area}} \times 100$

$$= \pi \frac{(4^2 - 3.75^2)}{\pi \times 4^2} \times 100 = \boxed{12.11\%}$$

HEAT

In Table 5.7, SI units for nine quantities that are encountered in Heat (including thermodynamics) are given. At all levels, the calorie has to be displaced by the joule and specific heat by specific heat capacity.

In Table 5.8, important thermal properties of various metals are given.

TABLE 5.7

SI UNITS IN HEAT

Quantity	Symbol for quantities	SI unit	Symbol for SI unit
Heat	—	joule	J
		millijoule	mJ
Heat flow rate	—	watt	W
		milliwatt	mW
Thermodynamic temperature	T	kelvin	K
Customary temperature	t	degree celsius	°C
Coefficient of linear expansion			K^{-1}
Thermal conductivity		watt/metre kelvin	W/(mK)
		watt/metre degree celsius	W/(m °C)
Coefficient of heat transfer	h	watt/square metre kelvin	W/(m² K)
		watt/square metre degree celsius	W/(m² °C)
Heat capacity	C	kilojoule/kelvin	kJ/K
		joule/kelvin	J/K
		kilojoule/degree celsius	kJ/°C
		joule/degree celsius	J/°C
Specific heat capacity	c	kilojoule/kilogram kelvin	kJ/(kg K)
		joule/kilogram kelvin	J/kg K
		kilojoule/kilogram degree celsius	kJ/(kg °C)
		joule/kilogram degree celsius	J/(kg °C)

NOTE: (1) Specific latent heat of water which in cgs units is 80 calories/gram becomes 333 kJ/kg in SI.

(2) Specific latent heat of steam which in cgs units is 539 calories/gram becomes 2260 J/g or, better, 2260 kJ/kg in SI units.

TABLE 5.8*

THERMAL PROPERTIES OF METALS

Metal	Melting point (K)	Sp. heat capacity J/(kg k)	Thermal conductivity W/(mk)	Coeff. of thermal expansion (MK^{-1})
Aluminium	933.3	875	234	24
Copper, pure	1356.2	386	384	17
Brass	1200	365	114	19
Phosphor bronze	1270		195	18
Gold	1336.2	128	310	14
Iron, pure	1812	438	75	12
Wrought			60	12
Cast	1500		48	9
Mild steel	1600	444	47	12
Lead	600.5	129	34.6	29
Magnesium	923	103	150	26
Mercury	234.3	140	8.4	
Nickel	1726.2	450	90	13
Platinum	2042.2	135	69.5	9
Silver	1234.0	234	418	19
Tin	505.1	224	64	23
Tungsten	3633	142	190	23
Zinc	692.7	387	111	26

*Extracted from SI units in Engineering by Deanne R. Blackman, Macmillan 1969, p. 36, Table 3.3.

LIGHT

Visible light is a part of the electromagnetic spectrum. In this spectrum, the wavelegnth range of visible light is between 8×10^{-7} to 4×10^{-7} m, which corresponds to the frequency range of 375 THz (terahertz) to 750 THz.

The wavelengths of the seven constituents of the visible spectrum both in nanometres (10^{-9} m) and angstrom units (Å) are given in Table 5.9. It is customary in the field of spectroscopy to use angstrom units.

1 nm $= 10^{-9}$m (nm stands for nanometre)

1Å $= 10^{-10}$m $= 10$ nm

TABLE 5.9

WAVELENGTHS IN THE VISIBLE SPECTRUM

Colour	Wavelength (λ)	
	in nm	in Å
Red	750–620	7500–6200
Orange	620–590	6200–5900
Yellow	590–580	5900–5800
Green	580–500	5800–5000
Blue	500–460	5000–4600
Indigo	460–450	4600–4500
Violet	450–400	4500–4000

Broadly speaking, we may say that the human eye responds to the band of wavelengths 400 to 700 nm, while the maximum response is at about 550 nm (green-yellow).

The following examples will illustrate the practical application of SI units in the field of illumination.

Example 23:   A lamp giving 100 cd in every direction below the lamp level, is suspended 6 m above above the floor level. Calculate: (*i*) the illumination at a point on the ground directly under the lamp, (*ii*) the total luminous flux within a circular area of 60 cm diameter.
Assume illumination to be uniform within this area.

Solution: $d = 60$ cm $= 0.6$ m; hence, $r = 0.3$ m
(*i*) The unit of illumination is lumen/m² or lux.
   The illumination under the lamp is
$$E = \frac{I}{h^2} = \frac{cd}{m^2} = \frac{100}{6^2} = \boxed{2.78 \text{ lx}}$$
(ii) Area of surface $\pi r^2 = 0.09 \pi$ m²
   Since the luminous flux per unit area is 2.87 lux, the total luminous flux $= 2.78 \times 0.09$
$$= \boxed{0.80 \text{ lm}}$$

NOTE: This problem uses the units: lux, candela and lumen.

Example 24:   Calculate the illumination (*a*) on a working plane at a point 3 metres vertically below a lamp emitting 720 cd, the surface is at right angles to the light source; (*b*) at a point *c*, 4 m from the point in (*a*) (Fig. 5-3).

Solution

(*a*)   Since $E = \dfrac{I}{d^2} = \dfrac{\text{Candela}}{\text{m}^2}$

$$E = \frac{720}{3^2} = \boxed{80 \text{ lx}}$$

(*b*) $E = \dfrac{I}{d^2} \times \cos\theta$.   Here $d = \sqrt{3^2 + 4^2} = 5$ m

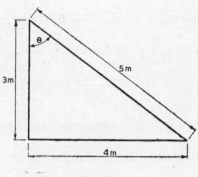

Hence $\cos\theta = \dfrac{3}{5} = 0.6$

$\therefore \quad E = \dfrac{720}{5^2} \times 0.6 \text{ lx}$

$$= \frac{720}{25} \times 0.6 \text{ lx} = \boxed{17.3 \text{ lx}}$$

Fig. 5.3

SOUND & ACOUSTICS

The SI unit of sound energy is the joule (J) but what we are more often interested is *sound power*. The SI unit of sound power is the *watt* (W)

Table 5.10 gives five quantities used in sound with the cgs units and their corresponding SI units.

TABLE 5.10

SI AND CGS UNITS IN SOUND

Quantity	cgs unit	SI equivalent
Sound energy flux	1 erg/second	10^{-7} W
Sound energy density	1 erg/cm²	10^{-3} J/m
Sound intensity	1 erg/second/cm²	1×10^{-3} W/m²
Audibility	1 cgs unit	1000 SI units
Acoustic impedance	1 acoustic ohm	10^5 SI acoustic ohms

Three common terms used will now be defined:

Intensity: The intensity of a sound is the power emitted through unit area and is usually measured in microwatts per square metre (μW/m²).

Relative intensity: When the intensity of one sound is 10 times that of another, its sound level is said to be one 'bel' higher than the other, i.e. the number of decibels (dB) $= 10 \log_{10} (I_2 / I_1)$ where I_1 is the first power and I_2 the second.

Loudness :   How loud a sound appears to be depends solely on the ear of the observer.   The unit of loudness is the 'phon.'   It is numerically equal to the relative intensity in dB above the threshold value of $10^{-18} \mu$ W m^{-2} of a standard note of 1000 Hz which the average person judges to be equally loud.

Example 25:   Find the wavelength of sound in air at a frequency of 100 Hz in metres.   Given volocity of sound in air is 344 m s^{-1}.

Solution: λ, the wave length $= \dfrac{v}{f}$ is in metres

v in m/s $= 344$ m/s f is in Hz

$$\therefore \ \lambda = \frac{344}{100} = \boxed{3.44 \text{ m}}$$

Example 26:   Determine the speed of sound at 21.1 °C.

Solution: Let v be the speed of sound in air in m/s.

Then $v = 20.05 \sqrt{T}$, where T is in kelvin

$$\therefore \ T = 273.15 + 21.1 \ = \ 294.25 \text{ K}$$

$$v \text{ (at 21.1 °C)} = 20.05 \sqrt{294.25} \ = \boxed{343 \text{ m/s}}$$

Example 27:   The rms pressure of sound is 2.0 N m^{-2}.   What is the sound pressure level?   Given reference pressure $= 0.000\,02$ Nm^{-2}.

Solution: Sound pressure level (SPL) $= 20 \log_{10} \times \dfrac{2}{0.000\,02} = 20 \log_{10} 10^5$

$$= 20 \times 5 = \boxed{100 \text{ dB}}$$

Example 28:   The intensity of a sound is 0.01 W m^{-2}.   What is the intensity level ?   Given reference intensity $= 10^{-12}$ W m^{-2}.

Solution: Intensity level (IL) $= 10 \log_{10} \dfrac{0.01}{10^{-12}} = 10 \log_{10} 10^{10} = \boxed{100 \text{ dB}}$

5.3.   SI units in Chemistry

In this article, the use of SI units in chemistry is explained by means of examples.

KILOGRAMME MOLECULAR WEIGHT

There is a very good case for making the kilogramme molecular weight* the seventh base unit in the SI system. This will mean a departure from the current practice of using the gram molecular weight. The mole as defined at present depends on the number of atoms in 0.012 kg of ^{12}C. It is not very difficult to redefine the mole as the number of atoms in 12 kg of ^{12}C. Consequently, Avogadro's number, the gas constant and the Faraday constant will have to be multiplied by 10^3. The use of the kilogramme molecular weight would obviate the need to deal with molecular weights less than 1.0. Other advantages that would follow in teaching physical chemistry will be evident from the examples given below:

Example I: Assuming Nitrogen to be an ideal gas, calculate its density under standard conditions.

Solution: One kilogramme-mole will have a mass of 28.0134 kg (molecular weight of nitrogen in kg). It will occupy a volume = 22.4136 m^3.

$$\text{Hence, density} = \frac{28.0134}{22.4136} = \boxed{1.2498 \text{ kg/m}^3}$$

Example II: Compute rms velocity of hydrogen molecules under standard conditions, if hydrogen is an ideal gas.

Solution: rms velocity $= \sqrt{\dfrac{3RT}{M}}$

$R = 8314.3$ J kmol^{-1} K^{-1}
$T = 273.15$
$M = 2.015\ 94$ kg

$$= \sqrt{\frac{3 \times 8314.3 \times 273.15}{2.015\ 94}} = \boxed{1838.4 \text{ m/s}}$$

NOTE: (*i*) If the gramme-molecule were used in Example I, the density would be 1.2498 gm/cm^3 $\times 10^{-3}$. This, surely, is not as convenient as 1.2498 kg/m^3.

(*ii*) If the gramme-molecule had been used in Example II, the rms velocity of hydrogen will be worked out as follows:

$$\text{rms velocity} = \sqrt{\frac{3 \times 8{,}317 \times 273.15 \times 10^3}{2.015\ 94}}$$
$$= 1838.4 \text{ m/s}$$

In this case the value of R is in J/gm-mole K^{-1} and it becomes necessary to introduce 10^3 in the numerator as J $= \dfrac{1 \text{ kg} \times 1 \text{ m}}{\sec^2}$. This factor is avoided by using the kilogramme-mole.

---

*Letter of Mr. L. W. Bean and Lenard Saunders on pp. 134—5 of *Chemistry in Britain*, Vol. 6, No. 3, March, 1970.

LAWS OF CHEMICAL COMBINATION

Example 29: Hydrogen is passed over samples of heated cupric oxide (CuO) and cuprous oxide (Cu_2O) of mass 0.00976 kg and 0.01 kg respectively. The copper obtained from the CuO and Cu_2O respectively were 0.008 kg and 0.009 kg. Show how this experiment illustrates the Law of Multiple Proportions.

Solution: The Law of Multiple Proportions may be stated as follows: *If two elements, C and D, form more than one chemical compound, the masses of D which combine with a fixed mass of C occur in the ratio of small whole numbers.*

Mass of CuO $\qquad\qquad$ = 0.009 76 kg
Copper obtained from CuO = 0.008 00 kg
Mass of oxygen in CuO $\quad$ = 0.001 76

Hence, 0.008 00 kg of copper combines with 0.001 76 kg of oxygen to form 0.009 76 kg of CuO.

$\therefore$ *1 kg of ccopper combines with* $\dfrac{0.008\ 00}{0.001\ 76}$ *kg = 0.22 kg of oxygen in CuO*

Mass of Cu_2O $\qquad$ = 0.01 kg
Mass of copper obtained from Cu_2O = 0.009 kg
Mass of oxygen in Cu_2O = 0.001

Hence, 0.009 kg of copper combines with 0.001 kg of oxygen to form cuprous oxide.

$\therefore$ *1 kg of copper combines with* $\dfrac{0.001}{0.009}$ *kg = 0.11 kg of oxygen to form Cu_2O.*

Now, the quantities 0.22 and 0.11 are in the simple ratio of 2:1, thus illustrating the Law of Multiple Proportions.

VAPOUR DENSITY AND MOLECULAR WEIGHTS

Example 30 : 0.000 187 kg of a volatile liquid on vaporisation occupies 0.000 035 6 m^3 at NTP. Calculate its vapour density and molecular weight assuming that 1 m^3 of H_2 weights 0.09 kg at NTP.

Solution : Vapour density = ratio between the weights of 1 m^3 of gas and 1 m^3 of H_2 at NTP.

$\therefore$ $\quad$ VD $=$ $\dfrac{\text{weight (in kg) of 1 } m^3 \text{ of gas at NTP}}{\text{weight of 1 } m^3 \text{ of } H_2 \text{ at NTP}}$

0.000 035 6 m^3 of vapour at NTP weights 0.000 187 kg

$\therefore$ $\quad$ 1 m^3 of vapour weighs $\dfrac{0.000\ 187 \times 1}{0.000\ 035\ 6}$ = 5. 25 kg.

$\therefore$ $\quad$ Density of vapour $\quad$ = 5.25 kg/m^3

$\therefore$ $\quad$ Vapour density $\qquad$ $= \dfrac{5.25}{0.09}$ = 58.3

$\qquad$ Molecular weight $\quad$ = 2 × vapour density

$\therefore$ $\quad$ Molecular weight of given vapour = 2 × 58.3 = $\boxed{116.6}$

GRAHAM'S LAW OF DIFFUSION

Example 31 : 0.05 litre of H_2 (0.000 05 m³) takes 600 seconds to diffuse out of a vessel. How long will 0.04 litre of O_2 take to diffuse out under similar conditions ?

Solution : Rate of diffusion of gas $= \dfrac{\text{volume of diffused gas}}{\text{time taken}}$

$\therefore$ Rate of diffusion of hydrogen $= \dfrac{0.05}{600}$

Similarly, rate of diffusion of $O_2 = \dfrac{0.04}{x}$, where $x =$ time for 0.04 litre of O_2 to diffuse.

$\dfrac{\text{Rate of diffusion of } H_2}{\text{Rate of diffusion of } O_2} = \dfrac{\text{density of oxygen}}{\text{density of hydrogen}}$

The densities being relative densities

$$\dfrac{0.05/600}{0.04/x} = \dfrac{16}{1}$$

i.e. $\dfrac{0.05\,x}{0.04 \times 600} = 4$ or $x = \boxed{1920 \text{ s}}$

CHEMICAL EQUATIONS

Example 32 : What volume of oxygen is liberated at NTP by heating 0.024 5 kg of potassium chlorate?

Solution : Potassium chlorate, on heating decomposes according to the equation

$\qquad 2\,KClO_3 \longrightarrow 2\,KCl + 3O_2$

$\qquad$ Kilogram molecular weight of $KClO_3 = 122.45$ kg

$\therefore$ 2 (122.45) gms $\longrightarrow 3 \times 22.4$ litres of O_2 at NTP

$\therefore$ 0.245 kg of $KClO_3$ yields 3×22.4 litres of O_2 at NTP

$\therefore$ 0.0245 kg will yield $\dfrac{67.2 \times 0.0245}{0.245}$ litres of O_2

$\qquad = 6.72$ litres of $O_2 = \boxed{0.006\ 72 \text{ m}^3 \text{ of } O_2}$

OSMOSIS

Example 33 : Calculate the osmotic pressure exerted by a 3% solution of cane sugar at 27 °C, given that the molecular weight of cane sugar is 342.

Solution : The gas equation $PV = RT$ holds good also for dilute solutions of non-electrolytes.

$\dfrac{PV}{T} = R =$ the universal gas constant $= 0.0821$ litre-atmospheres/gm-mole K

A gram-mole is a quantity of a substance whose weight is equal to the molecular weight in terms of grams. Hence 342 gms of cane sugar is to be considered. It has to be dissolved in $\frac{342}{3} \times 100$ gms = 11 400 gms having a volume of 11.4 litres.

Hence, $V = 11.4$ litres
$T = (273 + 27) = 300$ K
$$\frac{PV}{T} = R \text{ or } P = \frac{RT}{V} = \frac{0.0821 \times 300}{11.4} = \boxed{2.16 \text{ atmospheres}}$$

ELECTROLYSIS

Example 34 : A current of 0.1 A is passed for 2700 seconds through a voltameter containing acidulated water and another containing copper sulphate solution with copper electrodes. What volume of oxygen gas at NTP will be liberated in the first voltameter and what mass of copper will be deposited in the second voltameter?
(Take the ece of copper = 31.75×10^{-8} kg/c)

Solution: Since $m = e\,c\,t$, substituting the data in the formula
$$m = \frac{31.75}{96\,540} \times 0.1 \times 2700 = 0.08882 \text{ g of copper} = 0.08882 \times 10^{-3} \text{ kg of copper}$$

Since one molecular weight of oxygen occupies 22.4 litres at NTP, one equivalent weight of O_2 at NTP occupies $\frac{22.4 \times 8}{32} = 5.6$ litres. If in the formula $m = e\,c\,t$, this volume 5.6 litres is substituted in place of the equivalent weight, the result will be the equivalent volume.

$$\therefore \quad V = \frac{5.6}{96\,540} \times 0.1 \times 2700 = \boxed{0.015\,66 \text{ litres at NTP}}$$

Hence 0.015 66 litres of oxygen at NTP will be evolved.

FUELS AND COMBUSTION

Example 35 : A sample of fuel contains 84% carbon, 12.5 % hydrogen, 2% oxygen, 0.5% sulphur and 1% nitrogen. Calculate the minimum weight of air required for complete combustion of 100 kg of the fuel.

Solution

100 kg of fuel contains 84 kg of carbon
12.5 kg of hydrogen
2 kg of oxygen
0.5 kg of sulphur
1 kg of nitrogen

During combustion, the reaction between carbon and oxygen is:
$$C + O_2 \longrightarrow CO_2$$

12 kg of carbon require 32 kg of oxygen

$$\therefore \quad 84 \text{ kg require } \frac{32 \times 84}{12} = 224 \text{ kg of oxygen}$$

Similarly, $2H_2 + O_2 \longrightarrow 2H_2O$

4 kg of hydrogen require 32 kg of oxygen

$\therefore$ 12.5 kg require $\dfrac{32 \times 12.5}{4} = 100$ kg of oxygen

Finally, $S + O_2 \longrightarrow SO_2$

32 kg of sulphur require 32 kg of oxygen

$\therefore$ 0.5 kg of sulphur require 0.5 kg of oxygen

Nitrogen is not combustible.

Total quantity of oxygen required for perfect combustion

$$= 224 + 100 + 0.5 = 324.5 \text{ kg}$$

Oxygen already present in the fuel = 2 kg

$\therefore$ Net amount of oxygen required $= 324.5 - 2 = 322.5$ kg

Since the oxygen content in air by weight = 23%, amount of air required for perfect combustion of 100 kg of fuel

$$= \frac{322.5 \times 100}{23} = \boxed{1402.17 \text{ kg}}$$

Example 36 : A gaseous fuel has the following composition by volume: $H_2 = 12\%$, $CH_4 = 1.5\%$ CO = 24%, $CO_2 = 10\%$, $N_2 = 52.5\%$.

Calculate the minimum amount of air required for complete combustion of 100 m³ of the gas and the % compositions by volume of *dry* products of combustion.

Solution : The chemical reactions taking place during the combustion of the gaseous fuel are:

(i) $2H_2$ $+$ O_2 $\longrightarrow$ $2H_2O$

      (2 vols) $+$ (1 vol) $\longrightarrow$ 2 vols

(ii) CH_4 $+$ $2O_2$ $\longrightarrow$ CO_2 $+$ $2H_2O$

      (1 vol) $+$ (2 vols) $\longrightarrow$ (1 vol) $+$ (2 vols)

(iii) 2 CO $+$ O_2 $\longrightarrow$ $2CO_2$

      (2 vols) $+$ (1 vol) $\longrightarrow$ (2 vols)

      10 m³ of gas contains

          12 m³ of H_2

          1.5 m³ of CH_4

          24 m³ of CO

          10 m³ of CO_2

          52.5 m³ of N_2

From equation (i)

      12 m³ of H_2 require 6 m³ of O_2 for combustion

From equation (ii)

      1.5 m³ of CH_4 require 3 m³ of O_2 for combustion

From equation (iii)

      24 m³ of CO require 12 m³ of O_2 for combustion

CO_2 and N_2 are not combustible

$\therefore$ Total quantity of O_2 required $= 6 + 3 + 12 = 21$ m³

Composition of air by volume $= 21\% \; O_2 : 79\% \; N_2$

$\therefore$ Air required for combustion of the above fuel $= \dfrac{21 \times 100}{21} = \boxed{100 \; m^3}$

Calculation of the % *dry* products of combustion:

Volume of N_2 present in $100 \; m^3$ of air used for combustion $= 79 \; m^3$

Volume of N_2 originally present in the fuel $= 52.5 \; m^3$

     Total $N_2 = 131.5 \; m^3$

Volume of CO_2 obtained by the combustion of $CH_4 = 1.5 \; m^3$

Volume of CO_2 from CO $= 24 \; m^3$

Volume of CO_2 originally present in the fuel $= 10 \; m^3$

$\therefore$ Total CO_2 in the flue gases $= 35.5 \; m^3$

$\therefore$ Total volume of *dry* products of combustion $= 131.5 + 35.5 = 167 \; m^3$

$$\% \; CO_2 = \frac{35.5}{167} \times 100 = \boxed{21.3 \%}$$

$$\% \; \text{Nitrogen} = \frac{131.5}{167} \times 100 = \boxed{78.7 \%}$$

HYDROGEN ION CONCENTRATION (pH)

Example 37 : Calculate the *p*H value of a solution whose hydrogen ion concentration is 2.36×10^{-8} kg ion per m³.

Solution: $pH = - \log \; H^+ = - \log (2.36 \times 10^{-8}) = - \log (\overline{7}.6271) = - (-7.6271)$

$$= \boxed{7.6271}$$

NOTE : The result would be the same if the concentration were expressed as gram-ions per litre.

5.4 SI Units in Civil and Structural Engineering

The quantities that occur in Civil Engineering and the units in which they are best expressed are indicated in Table 5.11.

5.5 Conversion Factors

Conversion factors given below will be found useful in making calculations in SI.

LENGTH

1 in	= 25.4 mm	1 mm	= 0.039 37 in
1 ft	= 0.3048 m	1 m	= 39.37 in

AREA

1 in²	= 645.16 mm²	1 mm²	= 0.001 55 in²
1 ft²	= 0.092 903 m²	1 m m²	= 1 550 in²

VOLUME

1 in³	= 16 387 mm³	1 mm³	= 0.000 061 in³
1 ft³	= 0.028 317 m³	1 m³	= 610 23 in³

MOMENT OF INERTIA

1 in⁴	= 416 231 mm⁴	1 mm⁴	= 0.000 002 403 in⁴
1 ft⁴	= 0.008 63 mm⁴	1 m⁴	= 2 402 500 in⁴

FORCE

1 lbf	= 0.453 59 kgf	1 kgf	= 2.205 lbf
1 lbf	= 4.448 22 N	1 kgf	= 9.806 65 N
1 tonf	= 1 016 kgf	1 tonnef	= 2 205 lbf
1 tonf	= 9 964.012N	1 tonnef	= 9 806.65 N
	1 newton	= 0.102 kgf	
	1 newton	= 0.2248 lbf	

FORCE PER UNIT LENGTH

1 lbf/ft =1.488 16 kgf/m 1 kgf/m =0.671 97 lbf/ft
1 lbf/ft =14.59 N/m 1 kgf/m =9.806 65 N/m
1 tonf/ft =3333.4784 kgf/m 1 tonnef/m =671.970 lbf/ft
1 ton/ft =32 690 N/m 1 tonnef/m =9806.65 N/m
    1 N/m = 0.102 kgf/m
    1 N/m = 0.2248 lbf/m
    1 N/m = 0.0685 lbf/ft

BENDING MOMENT

1 lbf in =11.5212 kgf mm 1 kgf mm =0.007 234 lbf ft
1 lbf in =112.9 N mm 1 kgf mm =0.086 811 lbf in
1 lbf ft =0.138 254 kgf m 1 kgf mm =9.806 65 N mm
1 lbf ft =1.355 81 N m 1 kgf m =7.234 25 lbf ft
1 tonf in=25.807 45 kgf m 1 kgf m =86.811 07 lbf in
1 tonf ft=3037 N m 1 kgf m =9.806 65 N m
1 tonf in=253 084 N mm 1 tonnef mm=7.2342 lbf ft
1 tonf ft=309.688 kgf m 1 tonnef mm=86.811 07 lbf in
    1 tonnef mm=9806.65 N mm
1 N m =0.10 972 kgf m 1 tonnef m =7234.2558 lbf ft
1 N m =8.850 39 lbf in 1 tonnef m =86 811.07 lbf in
1 N m =0.737 533 lbf ft 1 tonnef m =9806.65 N m

PRESSURE AND STRESS

1 lbf/in²=0.000 703 kgf/ 1 kgf/mm² =1422.33 lbf/in²
      mm²
1 lbf/in²=0.006 895 N/ 1 kgf/mm² =9.806 65 N/mm²
      mm²
1 tonf/in²=1.575 kgf/mm 1 tonnef/m² =204.8 lbf/ft²
1 tonf/in²=15.444 N/m² 1 tonnef/m² =9806.65 N/m²
1 tonf/ft²=10 936.6 kgf/m² 1 tonf/ft²=107 251 N/m²
    1 N/m² = 0.102 kgf/m²
    1 N/m² = 0.000 145 lbf/in²
    1 N/m² = 0.020 87 lbf/ft²

DENSITY

1 lb/in³ =0.000 027 68 1 kg/mm³ =36 127.30 lb/in³
      kg/m³
1 lb/ft³ =16.018 5 kg/m 1 kg/m³ =0.000 036 127 3
        lb/in³

TABLE 5.11

CIVIL ENGINEERING UNITS

Quantity	Unit
Loads	
Uniformly distributed loads on an area	KN/m²
Wind load	N/m²
Uniformly distributed load per unit length	kN/m
Concentrated loads	kN
Stresses in materials	MN/m² or N/mm²
Bearing capacity of soil	kN/m²
Modulus of elasticity	MN/m² or N/mm²
Mass	kg and Mg (for large masses)
Bending moment and torque	N mm and kN m
Density in mass units	kg/m³
Density in force units	kN/m³*
Linear dimensions in drawings	mm
Linear dimensions in design calculations	m
Reinforcement spacing, rivet spacing, concrete cover, plate thickness	mm
Area	
Area of floor or foundation	m²
Area of cross-section of beam, area of reinforcing steel	mm²
Unit length of wall, beam and unit width of slab	m
Pressure	N/m²,; kN/m³
Density	kg/m³; g/litre
Velocity of flow	m/s
Pipe length	m
Pipe diameter	mm
Flow in small pipes	litre/s
Flow in channels and pipes	m³/s
Run-off from a catchment	m³/km²

5.6 Recognition Values

To get a feel of the magnitudes of quantities expressed in SI units in terms of the familiar units in the metric system, one may use an approximate conversion factor of 1 kgf ≈ 10 newton.

In dealing with stresses, it is useful to remember that 1 N/mm² = 1 MN/m² ≈ 10.2 kgf/cm² ≈ 145 lbf/in². Thus, a concrete cube

*In structural design, it is convenient to use force units

strength of 21 MN/m² in SI will correspond to 3000 lbf/in². Similarly a cube strength of 41 MN² would be equivalent to 6000 lbf/in². Cube strength of M 250 grade concrete according to IS Code 456 (cube strength = 250 kgf/cm²) would be 25 MN/m². Hence we may find it useful to remember the following:

CONCRETE	21 MN/m^2 $\approx$ 3000 lbf/in^2
CUBE STRENGTH	25 MN/m^2 $\approx$ 250 kgf/cm^2

BEARING CAPACITY OF SOILS	107.25 kN/m^2 $\approx$ 1 ton/ft^2

The following recognition values will be of help while dealing with loads and bearing pressures on foundations:

Type of occupancy	Live Load
OFFICE FLOORS	2.5 kN/m^2 $\approx$ 50 lbf/ft^2
FACTORY FLOORS	5.0 kN/m^2 $\approx$ 100 lbf/ft^2

5.7 Illustrative Examples

In the examples that follow, the use of SI in civil and structural engineering applications is explained in detail.

Example 38 : The roof of a lecture hall is a reinforced concrete slab 100 mm thick over T beams of 10 m span spaced 3 m apart. The superimposed load on the roof is 1.5 kN/m².

Arrive at the reinforcement at midspan given that 28 cube strength of the concrete is 20 MN/m² and the yield strength of high bond deformed bars is 425 MN/m².

Use the ultimate strength design method.

Solution

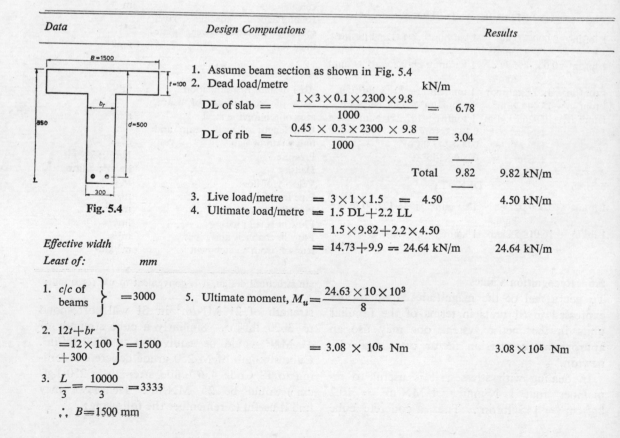

Data	Design Computations	Results
	1. Assume beam section as shown in Fig. 5.4	
	2. Dead load/metre kN/m	
	DL of slab $= \dfrac{1 \times 3 \times 0.1 \times 2300 \times 9.8}{1000} =$ 6.78	
	DL of rib $= \dfrac{0.45 \times 0.3 \times 2300 \times 9.8}{1000} =$ 3.04	
	Total 9.82	9.82 kN/m
Fig. 5.4	3. Live load/metre $= 3 \times 1 \times 1.5 =$ 4.50	4.50 kN/m
	4. Ultimate load/metre $=$ 1.5 DL$+$2.2 LL	
Effective width	$= 1.5 \times 9.82 + 2.2 \times 4.50$	
Least of: mm	$= 14.73 + 9.9 = 24.64$ kN/m	24.64 kN/m
1. c/c of beams $\}=3000$	5. Ultimate moment, $M_u = \dfrac{24.63 \times 10 \times 10^3}{8}$	
2. $12t+br$ $=12\times100$ $\}=1500$ $+300$	$= 3.08 \times 10^5$ Nm	3.08×10^5 Nm
3. $\dfrac{L}{3} = \dfrac{10000}{3} = 3333$		
$\therefore$, $B=1500$ mm		

Data	Design Computations	Results
Check span/depth	6. Assume the NA to lie within the flange at a distance a from the top (Fig. 5.5).	3.08×10^8 Nmm

$$\frac{L}{D} = \frac{10 \times 1000}{55}$$

< 20 o.k.

Equating external bending moment to the moment of resistance of the section,

$$0.55\, \sigma c_u \times B \times a \left(d - \frac{a}{2} \right) = M_u$$

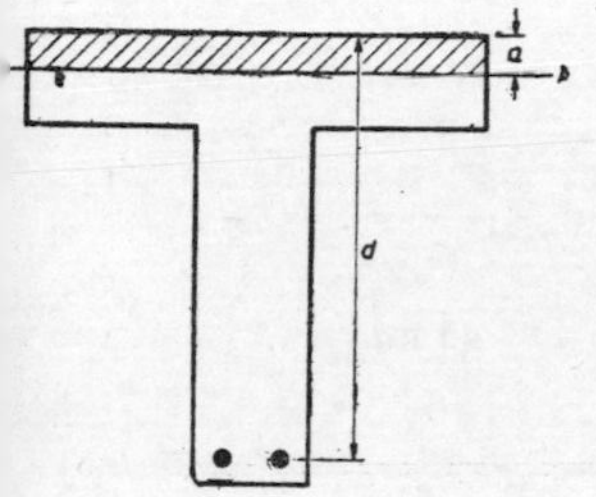

$$0.55 \times 20 \times 1500 \times a \left(500 - \frac{a}{2} \right)$$
$$= 3.08 \times 10^8$$

Solving $a = 39$ mm < 100 mm

Hence assumption o.k.

$a = 39$ mm

7. Compute area of steel. A_{st}

$$A_{st} = \frac{M_u}{\sigma_{sy} \left(d - \frac{a}{2} \right)} = \frac{3.08 \times 10^8}{425 \times (500 - 39)}$$

Fig. 5.5

$$= \boxed{1510 \text{ mm}^2}$$

$A_{st} = 1510$ mm²

Provide 5 ϕ 20 mm bars

with area $= \boxed{1570.8 \text{ mm}^2}$

5 ϕ 20 m

Example 39 : Select a suitable rolled steel joist to be used as a simply supported beam of span 12 metres to carry uniformly a load of 20 kN/m. Assume allowable stresses according to IS 800. Compute the mid-span deflexion.

Solution

Data	Design Computations	Results
Ref : IS 800	1. Load	
	Superimposed load $= 20$ kN/m	
$E_s = 2 \times 16^{11}$ N/m²	Assumee self weight $= 1$ kN/m	
Allowable bending stress	Total load $= 21$ kN/m	21 kN/m
$p_c = p_t = 160$ N/mm²	2. Maximum bending moment $\left. \right\} = \dfrac{21 \times 12 \times 12}{8}$	
Allowable shear stress	$= 378$ kN m	378 kN m
		$= 378 \times 10^3$ Nm
$= 90$ N/mm²		$= 378 \times 10^6$ Nmm
	3. Modulus of section Zxx required $\left. \right\} = \dfrac{378 \times 10^6}{160}$	
	$= 2.36 \times 10^6$ mm³	$= 2.36 \times 10^6$ mm³

Data	Design Computations	Results
	Referring to *I.S. Handbook for Structural Engineers,* ISMB 550 with $Zxx = 2359.8$ cm is selected	ISMB 550 $Zxx = 2359.8$ cm^3
Area of Web = 11.2×511.4 = 5727 mm^2	4. Maximum shear force $\left.\right\} = \dfrac{21 \times 1}{2} = 126$ kN	126 kN = 126×10^3 N
	5. Average shear stress in web $\left.\right\} = \dfrac{126 \times 10^3}{5727}$ $= 22$ N/mm^2 22 N/mm^2 < 90 N/mm^2 o.k.	22 N/mm^2
$I = 64\,893.6$ cm4 $= 64\,893 \times 10^4$ mm4	6. Deflexion = $\dfrac{5}{384} \times \dfrac{21 \times 12 \times 10^3 \times 12^3 \times 10^3)^3}{2 \times 10^{11} \times 64\,893 \times 10^4 \times 10^{-6}}$ $= \boxed{43 \text{ mm}}$	43 mm

Example 40 : The wall shown in Fig. 5.6 retains an earthfill with a density of 1600 kg/m³. The angle of internal friction ϕ of the granular soild behind the wall is 30°. The safe bearing capacity of the soil 1 metre below ground level is 107.251 kN/m². The allowable compressive and tensile stresses in the masonry are 2N/mm² in compression and 0.10342 N/mm² in tension respectively.

Check the stresses in the masonry and on the soil.

Solution

Data	Design Computations	Results
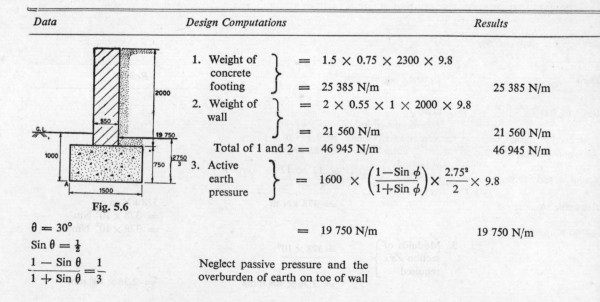 Fig. 5.6 $\theta = 30°$ Sin $\theta = \frac{1}{2}$ $\dfrac{1 - \text{Sin } \theta}{1 + \text{Sin } \theta} = \dfrac{1}{3}$	1. Weight of concrete footing $\left.\right\} = 1.5 \times 0.75 \times 2300 \times 9.8$ $= 25\,385$ N/m	25 385 N/m
	2. Weight of wall $\left.\right\} = 2 \times 0.55 \times 1 \times 2000 \times 9.8$ $= 21\,560$ N/m	21 560 N/m
	Total of 1 and 2 = 46 945 N/m	46 945 N/m
	3. Active earth pressure $\left.\right\} = 1600 \times \left(\dfrac{1 - \text{Sin } \phi}{1 + \text{Sin } \phi}\right) \times \dfrac{2.75^2}{2} \times 9.8$ $= 19\,750$ N/m	19 750 N/m
	Neglect passive pressure and the overburden of earth on toe of wall	

Data	Design Computations	Results
	4. Weight of earth on heel of wall $\left.\begin{array}{l}\\\\\end{array}\right\}$ $\begin{array}{l}= 0.475 \times 2 \times 1600 \times 9.8\\= 14\ 896 \text{ N/m}\end{array}$	14 896 N/m
	5. Total vertical load $P = 1+2+4 = 61\ 841$ N/m	64 841 N/m
	6. Compute eccentricity of the resultant on base of footing. Let resultant meet base at x mm from A. Taking moments about A,	
	$$14\ 896 \times 126 + 46\ 945 \times 750 - 19750 \times \frac{275}{3} = 61\ 841\ x$$	
	Solving $x = 580$ mm	
	eccentricity $e = \dfrac{1500}{2} - 580 = 170$ mm	$e = 170$ mm $e = 0.17$ m
$Z = \dfrac{1}{6} \times 1 \times 1.5^2$ $= 0.375$ m	7. Stresses on Soil $\dfrac{P}{A} \pm \dfrac{Pe}{Z} = \dfrac{64\ 841}{1.5} \pm \dfrac{64\ 841 \times 0.17}{0.375}$ $= 41\ 277 \pm 28\ 050$ N/m^2	
$A = 1 \times 1.5 = 1.5$ m^2	$= 69\ 277$ or 13 177 N/m^2 $69\ 277 < 10\ 725$ N/m^2 permissible	69 277 N/m^2 < 10 725 N/m^2. Hence o.k.
	8. Stress in masonry Direct load $= 21\ 560$ N Stress $= \dfrac{21\ 560}{550 \times 1000}$	
Area of wall $=$ 550 $\times$ 1000 $-$ 55 $\times$ 10 mm^2	0.0392 N/mm^2 Earth pressure on wall $=$ $1600 \times \dfrac{1}{3} \times \dfrac{2^2}{2} \times 9.8$ $= 10\ 453$ N	0.0392 N/mm^2 10 453 N
	Lever arm $= \dfrac{2000}{3} = 666.7$ mm	666.7 mm
Modulus of section of wall $= \dfrac{1}{6} \times 1000 \times 550^2$ mm^3 504 $\times 10^5$ mm^3	Bending moment at base of wall $\left.\begin{array}{l}\\\\\end{array}\right\} = 10\ 453 \times 666.7$ N/mm^2 Bending stress $= \dfrac{10\ 453 \times 666.7}{504 \times 10^5} = 0.1298$ N/mm^2	0.1298 N/mm^2
	Maximum compressive stress $\left.\begin{array}{l}\\\\\\\end{array}\right\}$ $\begin{array}{l}= 0.0392 + 0.1389\\\\0.1781 \text{ N/mm}^2\end{array}$	0.1781 N/mm^2 < 2N/mm^2 Hence o.k.
	Maximum tensile stress in masonry $\left.\begin{array}{l}\\\\\\\end{array}\right\}$ $\begin{array}{l}= 0.0392 - .1298 =\\\\0.100 \text{ N/mm}^2\end{array}$	0.10 N/mm^2 < 0.10342 N/mm^2 Hence o.k.

5.8 SI Units in Mechanical Engineering

The use of SI units in mechanical engineering is illustrated in the examples that follow.

Example 41 : A small generator is driven off the main engine through a steel shaft of 10 mm diameter and 0.20 m long. If the moment of inertia of the rotor is 3.0×10^{-3} kg m², determine its natural frequency in torsion assuming that the moment of inertia of the engine is very large compared to that of the generator.

Solution: According to the assumption made above, the engine end of the shaft can be idealized as fixed for the purpose of natural frequency calculation. Fig. 5.7 represents the mathematical model. From the theory of torsion, we have the relation

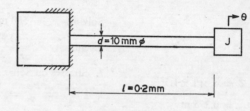

Fig. 5.7

$$k_t = \frac{T}{\theta} = \frac{GI_p}{l}$$

where k_t = Torsional stiffness in Nm/rad

T = Torque in Nm

θ = Angle of twist in rad

G = Shear modulus of the material of shaft in N/m²

I_p = polar moment of inertia of the area of shaft about the axis of twist in m⁴

l = length of shaft in m

$I_p = \dfrac{\pi d^4}{32}$ d being the diameter in m

Hence, substituting $d = 10 \times 10^{-3}$ m, $G = 8 \times 10^{10}$ N/m², $l = 2 \times 10^{-1}$ m

$$k_t = \frac{\pi (1 \times 10^{-2})^4 \times 8 \times 10^{10}}{32 \times 2 \times 10^{-1}} = \boxed{393 \text{ N m/rad}}$$

From the theory of vibrations, the expression for the undamped natural frequency of a torsional pendulam representing the present system, is given by :

$$f = \frac{1}{2\pi} \sqrt{\frac{k_t}{J}}$$

where f is in Hz and J is the mass moment of inertia of the disc about the axis of twist in kg m².

Substituting the values of k_t (= 393 Nm/rad) and J (= 3×10^{-3} kg m²)

$$f = \sqrt{\frac{393}{3 \times 10^{-3}}} = \boxed{57.6 \text{ Hz}}$$

Example 42 : Calculate the heat loss through a wall 0.25 m thick per square metre of surface, if the temperature difference across the faces is 100 K and the coefficient of conductivity is 0.6 W/mK.

Solution : Heat transmitted per second is given by $H = \dfrac{(kAT_1 - T_2)}{x}$

where
- k = coefficient of conductivity in W/mK = 0.60
- A = area in sq. metres = 1
- T = $(T_1 - T_2)$, temperature difference in kelvin = 100
- x = thickness of the medium in metres = 0.25

Substituting the given values,

$$H = \frac{0.6 \times 1.0 \times (100)}{0.25} = \boxed{240\ W}$$

Example 43 : A turbo-air compressor draws 6.0 m³ of air per second at a pressure of 1.0×10^5 N m⁻² absolute and a temperature of 300 K. The air is delivered from the compressor at 5.0×10^5 N m⁻² absolute and temperature 350 K. The area of the suction pipe is 0.2 m² and of discharge pipe 0.04 m² and the discharge pipe is 5 m above the suction inlet. The mass of jacket of water which enters at 300 K and leaves at 325 K is 6 kg per second. Find the power required to drive the compressor assuming no loss due to radiation.

Solution : Let 1 and 2 represent the inlet section and the outlet section respectively (Fig. 5.8). The energy equation will be :

Energy at inlet 1 $+$ Mechanical energy added to the compressor — Heat energy absorbed by jacket of water
$=$ Energy at the outlet 2

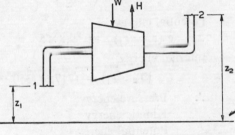

Fig. 5.8

Considering air of mass of one kilogramme,

$$\frac{p_1}{\rho_1} + \frac{v_1{}^2}{2} + mgz_1 + W - H + C_v T_1$$

$$= \frac{p_2}{\rho_2} + \frac{v_2{}^2}{2}\ mgz_2 + C_v T_2$$

Where
$\dfrac{p}{\rho_1}$ = $\dfrac{(pressure)}{(density)}$ = pressure energy in J kg⁻¹

$\dfrac{v_1{}^2}{2}$ = $\dfrac{(velocity)^2}{2}$ = (m/sec)² = kinetic energy in J kg⁻¹

gz_1 = (accn) (height) = (m/sec)² (m) = Potential energy in J kg⁻¹

$C_v T_1$ = (specific heat capacity) (temperature) = (J kg⁻¹ K⁻¹) (K) = internal heat energy in J kg⁻¹

W = Mechanical energy supplied in Joules per kg

H = Heat energy absorbed by jacket of water in Joules per kg

Rearranging, mechanical energy for 1 kg of air is

$$W = \left(\frac{p_2}{\rho_2} - \frac{p_1}{\rho_1}\right) + \left(\frac{v_2{}^2}{2} - \frac{v_1{}^2}{2}\right) + g\,(z_2 - z_1) + C_v\,(T_2 - T_1) + H$$

From the gas law $\dfrac{p}{\rho} = RT$, R being the gas constant J kg^{-1} K^{-1}

∴ Pressure energy

$$\left(\frac{p_2}{\rho_2} - \frac{p_1}{\rho_1}\right) = R(T_2 - T_1) = (287.045)(350 - 300) = 14352.25 \text{ J kg}^{-1}$$

Kinetic energy

$$v_1 = \text{Inlet velocity} = \frac{\text{volume/second}}{\text{area}} = \frac{6.0}{0.2} = 30 \text{ m/s}$$

$v_2 = $ Volume of air per second at outlet is given by

$$\frac{p_2 \, V_2}{p_1 \, V_1} = \frac{RT_2}{RT_1}$$

or,

$$V_2 = V_1 \times \frac{p_1}{p_2} \times \frac{T_2}{T_1} = 6.0 \times \frac{1}{5} \times \frac{350}{300} = 1.4 \text{ m}^3$$

$$\therefore \quad v_2 = \frac{1.4}{0.04} \quad 35 \text{ m/s per kg}$$

$$\therefore \quad \left(\frac{v_2{}^2 - v_1{}^2}{2}\right) = \frac{35^2 - 30^2}{2} = 162.5 \text{ J kg}^{-1}$$

Potential energy

$$g(z_2 - z_1) = 9.8 \times 5 = 49.0 \text{ J kg}^{-1}$$

Internal energy

$$C_v(T_2 - T_1) = (717.6)(350 - 300) = 35\,880 \text{ J kg}^{-1}$$

∴ Pressure energy   =   14 352.25
 Kinetic energy   =   162. 5
 Potential energy   =   49. 0
 Internal energy   =   35 880. 0

                50 443.75 J kg^{-1}

Mass of air per sec $= \dfrac{p_1 \, V_1}{RT_1} \times \dfrac{1}{\text{sec}}$ $= \dfrac{1 \times 6.0 \times 10^5}{(287.045)(300)}$

$$= \frac{1 \times 2 \times 10^3}{287.045} = 6.97 \text{ kg per}$$

Heat wasted in cooling water $= \text{m cp}(T_4 - T_3)$
                               $= 6 \times 4190 \times (325 - 300)$
                               $= 628\,500 \text{ Joules/s}$

Work done per second $= 6.97 \times 50\,443.75 + 628\,500$
                               $= 351\,593 + 628\,500$

                               $= 980\,093 \text{ Joules/s} = \boxed{980.093 \text{ k W}}$

5.9 SI Units in Electricity and Magnetism

Until recently, students of electricity and magnetism were obliged to deal with a bewildering variety of system of units. The more important among them are summarized in Table 5.12. Even an elementary study of electricity and magnetism involves at least three systems— Nos. 1, 2 and 5 in Table 5.12. The International System was discarded in 1948. The Gaussian System is still widely used in advanced physics and mathematics. The SI system has absorbed in itself systems 7 and 8. Hence, essentially SI replaces systems 1, 2, 5, 7 and 8.

5.10 Distinctive Features of RMKSA and SI Approach to Electricity and Magnetism

The introduction RmksA and SI systems of units has revolutionized the treatment of electricity and magnetism. The new approach calls for radical changes in teaching of these subjects. These changes have become necessary because of the new concepts underlying the SI system which are summarized below:

(i) The former definition of the ampere was in terms of its electrolytic effect. In the SI system, the ampere has become a a base unit and its definition is based on the magnetic effect of an electric current. This departure was motivated by the need to link the units of mechanics and electricity by establishing a relationship between the newton and the ampere, two base units of SI. Consequently, the volt, the ohm and the coulomb have become derived units.

(ii) Three new derived units with special names have been introduced. These are the weber (Wb) for magnetic flux, tesla (T) for magnetic flux density and henry (H) for inductance.

(iii) In SI, Joule is the only unit of energy and it is used for all forms of energy in magnetism, electricity and mechanics.

TABLE 5.12

SYSTEMS OF UNITS—COMMONLY USED IN ELECTERCITY AND MAGNETISM

S. No.	Abberivated Designation	Name of System
1.	emu	CGS electromagnetic system
2.	esu	CGS electrostatic system
3.	G	Gaussian
4.	H-L	Heaviside-Lorentz system
5.	Practical	Practical system (electromagnetic)
6.	Internat	International system (now obsolete)
7.	MKS	Metre-kilogram-second system
8.	RMKSA	Rationalised MKS Ampere system
9.	MIE	A rationalised system in Germany
10.	SI	Systeme International

(iv) Rationalized values have been introduced for ε_0 and μ_0 which are respectively known as the *permittivity* and *permeability* of *free space*.

(v) The unit of newton has been introduced as the unit of force.

(vi) The isolated point-pole approach has been replaced by the concept of uniform fields.

5.11 Rationalization

In the §5.10 we mentioned that SI has introduced rationalized values for ε_0 and μ_0. The rationalization introduced in SI involves, in effect, the restatement of two fundamental laws, the Coulomb's law and the Biot's law (Ampere's formula).

Let us first consider the Coulomb's law, the classical statement of which takes the form:

$$F = k \frac{qq'}{r^2} \tag{5.1}$$

where F is the force between two charges q and q' placed at a distance r apart. When other equations are developed from Coulomb's law, it is found that the factor 4π figures frequently. The occurrence of 4π in the wrong places stems from the concept of a unit magnetic pole from which one magnetic line of force is considered as emanating per unit area of surface of a sphere of unit radius. To eliminate the ubiquitous factor 4π, the constant k may be replaced by $1/4\pi\varepsilon_0$ so that

$$k = \frac{1}{4\pi\varepsilon_0\varepsilon_r} \qquad (5.2)$$

where ε_0 = permittivity of free space

ε_r = relative permittivity of a medium which is a pure number ($\varepsilon_r = 1$ for vaccum, and $\varepsilon_r = 1$ for air)

The product $\varepsilon_0\varepsilon_r = \varepsilon$ is known as absolute permittivity.

Coulomb's law may now be stated as

$$F = \frac{1}{4\pi\varepsilon_0\varepsilon_r} \frac{qq'}{r^2} \qquad (5.3)$$

In air or vacuum,

$$F = \frac{1}{4\pi\varepsilon_0} \frac{qq'}{r^2} \qquad (5.4)$$

The value of k in the classical statement of Coulomb's law is

$$8.98742 \times 10^9 \ \frac{Nm^2}{C^2} \approx 9 \times 10^9 \ \frac{Nm^2}{C^2}$$

Because $k = \dfrac{1}{4\pi\varepsilon_0}$

$$\varepsilon_0 = \frac{1}{4\pi k} = \frac{1 \times 10^{-9}}{4\pi \times 8.98742}$$

$$= 8.854 \times 10^{-12} \ \frac{C^2}{Nm^2}$$

The units in which ε_0 is expressed may be recast as follows:

$$\frac{C^2}{Nm^2} = \frac{C^2}{Jm^2} = \frac{C^2}{VAsm} = \frac{A^2s^2}{VAsm}$$

$$= \frac{As}{Vm} = \frac{1 \ Farad}{metre} = \frac{F}{m} \left(Because \ 1F = \frac{As}{V}\right)$$

Hence, $\boxed{\varepsilon_0 = 8.854 \times 10^{-12} \ \dfrac{F}{m}} \qquad (5.5)$

Coubomb's law in the cgs electrostatic system is stated as :

$$F = \frac{q\,q'}{r^2}$$

The unit of charge in this system is the stat coulomb. The unit of force is the dyne and the unit of distance is the centimetre. In this system the permittivity of free space is unity. *The stat coulomb is defined as that charge which repels an equal charge of the same sign with a force of 1 dyne when the two charge are placed one centimetre apart.*

Hence,

$$1 \ dyne = \frac{(1 \ stat \ coulomb)^2}{cm^2}$$

1 Coulomb $= 2.99790 \times 10^9$ stat coulombs

Let us next consider the Biot's Law (Ampere rule) which needs restatement in the SI system. The law is usually stated as :

$$\triangle B = k' \frac{i \triangle l \sin\theta}{r^2} \qquad (5.6)$$

where $\triangle B$ represents the magnetic flux at a point P (Fig. 5.9) caused by an element of a conductor carrying a current i in the direction shown; r is the distance of the point P; and θ, the angle made by the line joining the element

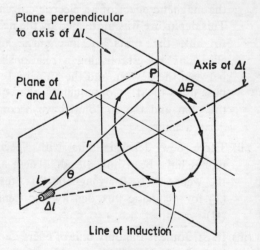

Fig. 5.9
Magnetic field due to a current element

conductor to P. $\triangle B$ is a vector and its direction is as shown in Fig. 5.9. In vector notation,

$$\triangle \mathbf{B} = k' i \frac{\triangle \mathbf{l} \times \mathbf{r}}{r^2}$$ where $\mathbf{r}$ is a unit vector in

the direction of r (Fig. 5.9). The vector $\triangle \mathbf{B}$ lies at right angles to the plane of the paper. Equations based on Biot's Law are more often used than the law itself. To eliminate 4π from the expressions based on Biot's law, we may restate the law as follows:

$$\triangle B = \frac{\mu_0}{4\pi} \frac{i \triangle l \sin \theta}{r^2} \tag{5.7}$$

where μ_0 is the permeability of free space. We introduce two other terms μ_r and μ which are defined below:

μ_r = relative permeability of a medium

$\quad = \dfrac{\text{Flux density produced in a medium}}{\text{Flux density produced in free space}}$

$\mu_r = \mu_0 \mu$

It is clear that μ_r is a pure number and is dimensionless; μ_r value is taken as unity for air and vacuum. The flux density $\triangle B$ is expressed in

$$\frac{\text{weber}}{\text{metre}^2} \rightarrow \frac{\text{Wb}}{\text{m}^2} \text{ where } 1 \text{ Wb} = 1\text{V} \times 1\text{s} = \text{Vs}$$

The unit $\dfrac{\text{Wb}}{\text{metre}^2}$ is given the special name of Tesla (T). Hence, $\text{T} = \text{Wb m}^{-2}$.

Let us next consider a special case of an infinitely long conductor carrying a current i (Fig. 5.10). Consider a point P at a perpendicular distance of a from the conductor. The magnetic flux B at the point found from Biot's law given in eqution 5.7 is

$$B = \frac{\mu_0}{2\pi} \frac{i}{a} \tag{5.8}$$

If now a parallel conductor carrying a current i' is placed at P so that the distance between the two conductors is a, a force will develop between the two conductors. The force F over a length l of the upper conductor (Fig. 5.11) will be

$$F = iBl = \frac{\mu_0}{4\pi} l \frac{2ii'}{a} \tag{5.9}$$

The force F will be in the plane defined by the two parallel conductors. This will be clear if it is realized that F is the vector product of B and l. Recalling the new definition of the ampere, it is evident that the force F which develops between the two conductors is $2 \times 10^7 \text{N}$, if $l = 1$ m $i = i' = 1$ A and $a = 1$ m.

Hence,

$$2 \times 10^{-7} \text{ newtons} = \frac{\mu_0}{2\pi} \times \text{ampere}^2$$

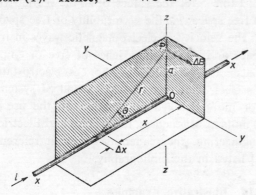

Fig. 5.10

Magnetic field set up by the current in an element $\triangle x$ of a long straight conductor

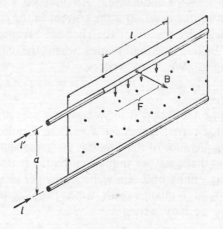

Fig. 5.11

Parallel conductors carrying currents in the same direction attract each other

$$\mu_o = 4\pi \times 10^{-7} \frac{N}{A^2}$$

$$= 1.257 \times 10^{-7} \frac{N}{A^2}$$

$$\frac{N}{A^2} = \frac{J}{mA^2} = \frac{VAs}{mA^2} = \frac{Vs}{Am}$$

But,

$$\frac{1 \text{ volt} \times 1 \text{ sec}}{1 \text{ ampere}} = 1 \text{ henry}$$

Therefore, $\dfrac{N}{A^2} = \dfrac{H}{m} = H\ m^{-1}$ henry per metre.

Hence, $\boxed{\mu_o = 1.257 \times 10^{-7}\ H\ m^{-1}}$ (5.10)

The *permeability* of a medium is B/H, where B is the flux density and H the magnetising force. The *magnetic flux density B* at a point is the magnetic flux per unit area normal to the flux. It is a vector having the same direction as the magnetising flux. In a uniform field, the flux $\phi = BA$ where A is the area normal to B.

5.12 Self Induced Electromotive Force

Let us consider a coil of N turns connected in series with a seat of emf and rheostat and linked by ϕ lines of induction. An induced electromotive force is set up if the current in the circuit is varied by means of the rheostat because the flux linking the coil varies when the current changes. We may write:

$$N\phi = Li \qquad (5.11)$$

Because the flux ϕ is in webers, the unit of $N\phi$ is weber-turns; $L = N\phi$ if $i = 1$. L is called the self inductance of the circuit. It is the number of flux linkages per unit of current. It is clear that the units of L are weber-turns per ampere. If ϕ and i change with time, from equation (5.11) we may write,

$$N\frac{d\phi}{dt} = L\frac{di}{dt} \qquad (5.12)$$

If self induced emf is $\mathscr{E}$, we know that

$$\mathscr{E} = -N\frac{d\phi}{dt} \qquad (5.13)$$

Substituting this relation in equation (5.12),

$$\mathscr{E} = -L\frac{di}{dt} \qquad (5.14)$$

The minus sign indicates that the self induced emf is in a direction opposite to the 'cause'. From equation (5.14), it is clear that the induced emf is not proportional to the current but to the change in current. The implication of the minus sign is that the induced emf and the current are in the same direction, if the current is decreasing; they oppose each other if the current is increasing. In equation (5.14), the inductance L is expressed in henrys (H) and the emf $\mathscr{E}$ in volts. Hence it may be deduced from equation (5.14) that:

$$1\ H = 1\ \frac{Vs}{A} \qquad (5.15)$$

5.13 Important Constants in Different Unit Systems

In Table 5.13, the values of ε_o, the permittivity of free space; μ_0, the permeability of free space; c, the velocity of electromagnetic waves in free space and Z_0, the impedance of free or empty space are presented in the cgs electrostatic, cgs electromagnetic, the MKS and SI systems. For more detailed information on the use of SI units in Magnetism, Electronics and Electrical Engineering, the reader may consult reference [1] listed in the bibliography.

5.14 Illustrative Examples

In the examples that follow the use of SI in electrical engineering is explained.

TABLE 5.13

VALUES OF ε_0, μ_0, c AND Z_0 IN DIFFERENT SYSTEMS OF UNITS

Constant	System			
	CGS electrostatic	CGS electromagnetic	MKS (unrationalised)	SI or Rationalised MKSA
Permittivity of free space, ε_0	1	$\dfrac{1}{9 \times 10^{20}}$	$\dfrac{1}{9 \times 10^9}$	$\dfrac{10^{-9}}{36\pi}$ $=8.85$ pF/m
Permeability of free space, μ_0	$\dfrac{1}{9 \times 10^{20}}$	1	$\dfrac{1}{10^7}$	$\dfrac{4\pi}{10^7}$ $= 1.257\ \mu$ H/m
Velocity of electromagnetic waves in free space, $c = \sqrt{\dfrac{1}{\mu_0\,\varepsilon_0}}$	3×10^{10} cm/s	3×10^{10} cm/s	3×10^8 m/s	3×10^8 m/s
Impedance of empty or free space, $Z_0 = \sqrt{\dfrac{\mu_0}{\varepsilon_0}}$	$\dfrac{1}{3 \times 10^{10}}$ CGS esu of resistance	3×10^{10} CGS em units of resistance	$30\ \Omega$	$4\pi \times 30\ \Omega$ $= 377\ \Omega$

Example 44: A solenoid of length 20 cm and radius 2 cm is closely wound with 100 turns of wire. The current in the winding is 5 amperes. Find the magnetic induction at a point near the centre of the solenoid.

Solution: It can be easily shown that the magnetic induction B at the centre of solenoid is given by:

$$B = \frac{\mu_0 N i}{l}$$

where μ_0 = the coefficient of permeability of free space in Hm^{-1}

$\quad N$ = number of turns

$\quad i$ = current in amperes

$\quad l$ = length of the solenoid

It may be noted that the radius of the solenoid does not enter the problem so long as it is small compared to its length.

In this problem,

$$\mu_o = 4 \times 10^{-7} \text{ Hm}^{-1}$$
$$N = 100$$
$$i = 5A$$
$$l = 20 \text{ cm} = 20 \times 10^{-2} \text{ m}$$

Substituting these values in the expression for B,

$$B = \frac{4\pi \times 10^{-7} \times 100 \times 5}{20 \times 10^{-2}}$$

$$= \pi \times 10^{-3} = 3.14 \times 10^{-3} \text{ tesla} = \boxed{3.14 \times 10^{-3} \text{ T}}$$

Example 45: A certain moving coil galvanometer produces a deflection of 100 mm on a scale at 2 m distance when a current of 1A is passed through it. When swinging freely on open circuit, the period is observed to be 3.5 s. The galvanometer is dead-beat with a total circuit resistance of 2500 ohms. Compute the moment of inertia of the moving system. Neglect air-friction damping.

Solution: The equation of motion of the galvanometer is

$$a \frac{d^2\theta}{dt^2} + b\frac{d\theta}{dt} + c\theta = gi$$

where
a = the moment of inertia of the moving system in kg m^2
b = the damping torque constant in Nm rad^{-1} s
c = the control torque constant in Nm rad^{-1}
g = the driving torque constant in Nm A^{-1}
θ = the angular deflection in radians of the moving system from the zero position

If the angular deflection of the moving system is θ, that of the reflected ray on sacle = 2θ.

$$2\theta = (0.1/2) = (1/20)$$
$$\therefore \theta = 1/40 \text{ rad}$$

From the static sensitivity,

$$gi = c\theta$$
$$g \times 10^{-6} = c \times (1/40)$$
$$(g/c) = (1/4) \times 10^5 \text{ A}^{-1} \tag{1}$$

When swinging freely, natural period

$$T_0 = 2\pi \sqrt{(a/c)} = 3.5 \text{ s}$$

$$\therefore \quad (a/c) = \left(\frac{3.5}{2\pi}\right)^2 \text{ s}^2 \tag{2}$$

From (1) and (2),

$$(g/a) = (10^5/4)(2\pi/3.5)^2 \text{ A}^{-1} \text{ s}^{-2} \tag{3}$$

Since air-friction is neglected, $b = (g/R)$, where R is the total circuit resistance in ohms. For critical damping,

$$(g /2aR) = \sqrt{(c/a)}$$

$$(g/a)\,(g/2R) = \sqrt{(c/a)} \tag{4}$$

From (2), (3) and (4),

$$(10^5 /4)\,(2\,\pi/3.5)^2 \times (g/5000) = (2\pi /3.5)$$

$$g = (3.5/2\,\pi) \times (4/10^5) \times 5000$$

$$= (0.35/\pi)\ \text{Nm A}^{-1} \tag{5}$$

From (3) and (5)

$$a = (4/10^5)\,(3.5/2\pi)^2 \times g$$

$$= 10^{-5}\,(3.5^2/\pi^3)\,0.35\ \text{kg. m}^2 \quad = \quad \boxed{1.383\ \text{kg. mm}^2}$$

Example : 46 A 220 V, 4-pole, series motor has a lap-connected armature winding housed in 40 slots with 30 conductors per slot. The useful flux per pole is 25 mWb, with a line current of 50A. The armature and field resistances are 0.4 and 0.25 ohm respectively. Calculate:

(a) the pull at the end of an 1 m arm dynamometer used to measure the developed torque,
(b) the power developed.

Solution : (a) Torque developed in Nm, $T = \dfrac{1}{2\,\pi}\,(p\phi)\,(I_a\,Z_a)$

where p = is the number of poles

ϕ = the fulx per pole, Wb

I_a = the armature current, A

Z_a = the number of conductors per parallel path of the armature

R_a = armature resistance in Ω

R_f = field resistance in Ω

In this problem

$$p = 4 = 2.5 \times 10^{-3}\ \text{Wb}$$

$$I_a = 50\text{A}$$

$$Z_a = \frac{40 \times 30}{4} = 300$$

$\therefore$ $T = (1/2\pi) \times 4 \times 2.5 \times 10^{-3} \times 50 \times 300 = 150/2\pi\ \text{N m}$

$$R_a = 0.40\ \Omega$$

$$R_f = 0.25\ \Omega$$

$$T = F \times r$$

where r is the torque arm.

> Pull at the end of the dynamometer arm $= 150/2\pi$ N

(b) With the usual notation, induced emf

$$E_b = V - I_a (R_a + R_f) = 220 - 50 (0.4 + 0.25) = 220 - 32.5 = 187.5 \text{ V}$$

> Power developed,
> $$E_b I_a = 187.5 \times 50 \times 10^{-3} \text{ kW} = 9.375 \text{ kW}$$

Example 47 :   A 200 km length of single phase concentric cable takes a charging current of 120 A when connected to a 11 kV, 50 Hz busbars.   The inner conductor has a diameter of 6 mm and the insulation is 4 mm in radial thickness.   Find the relative permittivity of the deielectric.

Solution : Capacitance of the cable,

$$C = \frac{I}{V\omega} = \frac{120}{11 \times 10^3 \times 314} = \frac{120 \times 10^{-3}}{11 \times 314} \text{ F}$$

Capacitance per metre length $= \dfrac{120 \times 10^{-6}}{11 \times 200 \times 314} \text{ F}$

It is also equal to $\dfrac{2\pi \varepsilon_0 \varepsilon_r}{\ln(b/a)} \text{ F}$

In this problem

$$
\begin{aligned}
a &= 6 \text{ mm} \\
b &= 14 \text{ mm} \\
\varepsilon_0 &= 8.85 \times 10^{-12} \text{ F/m} \\
(b/a) &= (7/3)
\end{aligned}
$$

$$\varepsilon_r = \frac{120 \times 10^{-3}}{11 \times 200 \times 314} \times \frac{\ln(7/3)}{2 \times 8.85 \times 10^{-12}} = \boxed{2.644}$$

Appendix I

THE STANDARDS OF WEIGHTS AND MEASURES ACT,*

1956 (No. 89 of 1956)

(as amended in 1960 and 1964)

An Act to establish standards of weights and measures based on the metric system

BE it enacted by Parliament in the Seventh Year of the Republic of India as follows :

SHORT TITLE, EXTENT AND COMMENCEMENT

1. (1) This Act may be called the Standards of Weights and Measures Act, 1956.*

(2) It extends to the whole of India.

(3) It shall come into force on such date, not being later than ten years from the passing of this Act, as the Central Government may, by notification in the Official Gazette, appoint; and different dates may be appointed for different provisions of this Act or for different areas or for different classes of undertakings or for different classes of goods :

Provided that, in relation to the State of of Jammu and Kashmir, the said period of

*The Standards of Weights and Measures Act, 1956 (No. 89 of 1956) received the President's assent on 28th December 1956. It was amended in 1960 and 1964.

ten years shall be computed from the date on which the STANDARDS OF WEIGHTS AND MEASURES (AMENDMENT) ACT, 1960 comes into force.

DEFINITIONS

2. In this Act, unless the context otherwise requires,

(a) 'First General Conference of Weights and Measures' means the Conference Generale des Poids et Mesures held at Paris in 1889;

(b) 'International Bureau of Weights and Measures' means the Bureau International des Poids et Mesures at Servres in France;

(c) 'Kilogram' means the mass of the platinum-iridium cylinder deposited at the International Bureau of Weights and Measures and declared international prototype of the kilogram by the First General Conference of Weights and Measures;

(d) 'metre' means the length equal to 1 650 763.73 wavelengths, in vacuum, of the radiation corresponding to the transition between the $2p_{10}$ and $5d_5$ levels of the krypton atom of mass 86;

(e) 'normal atmospheric pressure' means the pressure exercised by 101 325 newtons per square metre, a newton being the force which imparts to a mass of one kilogram an acceleration of one metre per second per second.

PRIMARY UNIT OF LENGTH

3. (1) The primary unit of length shall be a metre.

(2) For the purpose of deriving the value of the metre, the Central Government shall cause to be prepared a national prototype of the metre and shall cause the same to be certified by the International Bureau of Weights and Measures and shall deposit the same in such custody and at such place as the Central Government may think fit.

PRIMARY UNIT OF MASS AND STANDARD UNIT OF WEIGHT

4. (1) The primary unit of mass shall be a kilogram.

(2) For the purpose of deriving the value of kilogram, the Central Government shall cause to be prepared a national proto-type of the kilogram and shall cause the same to be certified in terms of the international proto-type of kilogram and shall deposit the same in such custody and such place as the Central Government may think fit.

(3) Notwithstanding anything contained in sub-section (1) of this section and section 12, the primary unit of mass for precious stones shall be a carat which is equal to one-five thousandth of one kilogram.

(4) The standard unit of weight at any place shall be the weight of the primary unit of mass at that place.

UNIT OF TIME

5. (1) The primary unit of time shall be a second.

(2) A second means 1/31 556 925.974 7 of the length of the tropical year for 1900.0, the year commencing at 1200 hours universal time on the 1st day of January, 1900.

UNIT OF ELECTRIC CURRENT

6. (1) The unit of electric current shall be an ampere.

(2) An ampere means that constant current which, flowing in two parallel straight conductors of infinite length, of negligible circular cross-section and placed at a distance of one metre from each other in vacuum, produces a force of 2×10^{-7} newtons per metre length between the conductors.

SCALE OF TEMPERATURE

7. The scale of temperature shall be the Centigrade scale otherwise known as Celsius where the temperature, under normal atmospheric pressure, is taken to be zero degree at the melting point of ice and one hundred degrees at the boiling point of water.

UNIT OF LUMINOUS INTENSITY

8. (1) The unit of luminous intensity shall be the candela.

(2) A candela means one-sixtieth part of luminous intensity normally emitted by one centimetre square of integral radiator (black body) at the temperature of solidification of platinum.

PRIMARY UNIT OF AREA

9. The primary unit of area shall be the square metre.

PRIMARY UNIT OF VOLUME

10. The primary unit of volume shall be the cubic metre.

UNIT OF CAPACITY

11. The unit of capacity shall be a litre which is the volume occupied by the mass of one kilogram of pure air-free water at the temperature of its maximum density and under normal atmospheric pressure.

SECONDARY UNITS OF MASS AND MEASURES

12. The Central Government may, by notification in the Official Gazette, declare in relation to the units of mass and measures referred to in sections 3 and 4 and sections 9 to 11, both inclusive, the magnitude and denominations of such units of mass and measures as it thinks fit to be the secondary units of mass and measures under this Act; provided that every such secondary unit shall be an integral power of ten (positive or negative) of any one of such units.

STANDARDS OF MASS AND MEASURES

13. (1) The units of mass and measures referred to in sections 3 and 4 and sections 9 to 11, both inclusive, and the secondary units of mass and measures declared under section 12 shall be the standards of mass and measures.

(2) No unit of mass or measure other than the units of mass and measures referred to in sub-section (1) shall be used as a standard or measure.

CONTINUANCE OF CERTAIN WEIGHTS AND MEASURES DURING TRANSITIONAL PERIOD

14. (1) Not withstanding that this Act has come into force in respect of any area or class of goods or undertakings, the Central Govern-ment may, by notification in the Official Gazette, permit the continuance of the use, after such commencement, in respect of that area or class of goods or undertakings, of such weights and measures, in addition to the standards of mass and measures and for such period, not exceeding three years, as may be specified in the notification.

(2) Nothing in sub-section (1) shall be deemed to empower the Central Government to issue any such notification in respect of any weight or measure which was not in use immediately before the commencement of this Act.

SETS OF STANDARDS OF MASS AND MEASURES

15. (1) The Central Government shall cause to be prepared as many sets as it may deem necessary of such standards of mass and measures referred to in section 13 or multiples of sub-multiples thereof as the Central Government may consider expedient, and shall cause each mass and measure of such set to be authenticated as having been ascertained from the primary units of mass or measure, as the case may be.

(2) The Central Government shall supply to each of the State Governments as many such sets as it may deem fit.

15A. 'Notwithstanding anything contained in this Act, a nautical mile which is equal to 1 852 metres, may be used as the unit of length in relation to navigation by sea or air'.

CONVERSION OF EXISTING WEIGHTS AND MEASURES INTO STANDARD MASS AND MEASURES

16. (1) The value expressed in terms of any weight set forth in sub-section (1) of section 3 of the Standards of Weight Act, 1939 (9

of 1939) or in terms of any measure expressed in inches, feet, yards or miles or in gallons may be converted into the value expressed in terms of a standard mass or measure at the rates specified in the First Schedule.

(2) The Central Government may, by notification in the Official Gazette, specify the rates at which the value expressed in terms of any weight or measure other than those referred to in sub-section (1) may be converted into the value expressed in terms of a standard mass or measure.

(3) All references in any enactment or in any notification, rule or under any enactment or in any contract, deed or other instruments to a value expressed in terms of any weight or measure other than those of a standard mass or measure shall be construed as reference to that value expressed in terms of a standard mass or measure, as the case may be, converted there to at the rates specified in the First Schedule or in the notification issued under sub-section (2), as the case may be.

(4) Where in any transaction the value expressed in terms of any weight or measure is required to be converted into that value expressed in terms of a standard mass or measure under this section, the calculation, for the purposes of such transaction, shall be made in such manner as may be prescribed by rules.

POWER TO MAKE RULES

17. (1) The Central Government may, by notification in the Official Gazette, make rules to carry out the purposes of this Act.

(2) In particular, and without prejudice to the generality of the foregoing power, such rules may provide for all or any of the following matters, namely :

(a) the preparation of the standards of mass and measures under section 15;

(b) the custody of the set of standards of mass and measures which are to be maintained by the Central Government and the periodical verification and adjustment thereof;

(c) the periodical verification and adjustment of sets of standards of mass and measures supplied to the State Governments;

(d) the limits of error which may be tolerated in the standards of mass and measures when they are manufactured for being used, or are being used, in transactions generally, or in any class of transactions in particular;

(e) the manner in which the value expressed in terms of any weight or measure other than in terms of a standard mass and measure may be converted thereto; and

(f) any other matter which has to be, or may be, prescribed.

(3) Every rule made under this section shall be laid as soon as may be after it is made, before each House of Parliament while it is in session for a total period of thirty days which may be comprised in one session or in two successive sessions, and if before the expiry of the session in which it is so laid or the session immediately following, both Houses agree in making any modification in the rule or both Houses agree that the rule should not be made, the rule shall thereafter have effect only in such modified form or be of no effect, as the case may be, so however that any such modification or annulment shall be without prejudice to the validity of anything previously done under that rule.

REPEAL

18. (1) The Measures of Length Act, 1889 (2 of 1889) and the Standards of Weight Act, 1939 (9 of 1939) are hereby repealed.

(2) The enactments specified in the Second Schedule shall, to the extent to which they contain any provision which corresponds to any provision of the Act, stand repealed.

(3) If, immediately before the commencement of this Act, or any provision thereof in respect of any area or class of goods or undertakings, there is in force in respect of that area or class of goods or undertakings, any law which corresponds to this Act, or to any provision thereof and which is not repealed by sub-section (1) or sub-section (2), that corresponding law shall stand repealed.

THE FIRST SCHEDULE
(See Section 16 (1))

Standards of Weight

1 gram	=	0.000 064 799	kilogram
1 ounce	=	0.028 349 5	kilogram
1 pound	=	0.453 592 4	kilogram
1 cwt	=	50.802	kilogram
1 ton	=	1 016.05	kilograms
1 tola	=	0.011 663 8	kilograms
1 seer	=	0.933 10	kilogram
1 maund	=	37.324 2	kilogram

Standards of Length and Capacity

1 inch	=	0.025 4	metre (exact)
1 foot	=	0.304 8	metre (exact)
1 yard	=	0.914 4	metre (exact)
1 mile	=	1 609.344	metre (exact)
1 imperial gallon	=	4.545 96	litre

THE SECOND SCHEDULE
[See section 18(2)]

1. The Assam Adoption of Standard Weights Act, 1955 (IX of 1955).
2. The Bhopal State Weights and Measures Act, 1953 (XV of 1953).
3. The Bihar Weights Act, 1947 (XVII of 1947).
4. The Bombay Weights and Measures Act, 1932 (XV of 1932).
5. The Central Provinces and Berar Weights and Measures of Capacity Act, 1928 (II of 1928).
6. The Cochin Weights and Measures Act, 1112 (LXIII of 1112).
7. The Coorg Act, 1954 (VII of 1954).
8. The Hyderabad Weights and Measures Act, 1356 Fasli (XIV of 1356 Fasli).
9. The Madhya Bharat Weights Act, 1954 (21 of 1954).
10. The Madras Weights and Measures Act, 1948 (XXII of 1948) as in force in the State of Madras or of Andhra.
11. The Mysore Weights and Measures Act, 1902 (III of 1902).
12. The Orissa Weights and Measures Act, 1943 (VII of 1943).
13. The Punjab Weights and Measures Act, 1941 (XII of 1941).
14. The Rajasthan Weights and Measures Act, 1954 (XIX of 1954).
15. The Travancore Weights and Measures Act, 1085 (VI of 1085).
16. The United Provinces Weights and Measures Act, 1947 (XXIII of 1948).

Appendix II

DEFINITIONS OF THE BASE UNITS OF THE SI

The definitions of the six base units as recognised by the General Conference of Weights and Measures are given below.

Length

The *metre* is the length equal to 1 650 763.73 wavelengths in vacuum of the radiation corresponding to the transition between the levels $2p^{10}$ and $5d_5$ of the krypton-86 atom. [11th CGPM (1960), Resolution 6]

Mass

The *kilogram* is the unit of mass; it is equal to the mass of the international prototype of the kilogram. [1st and 3rd CGPM (1889) and (1901)]

Time

The *second* is the duration of 9 192 631 770 periods of the radiation corresponding to the transition between the two hyperfine levels of the ground state of the caesium-133 atom. [13th CGPM (1967) Resolution 1]

Intensity of Electric Current

The *ampere* is that constant current which, if maintained in two straight parallel conductors of infinite length, of negligible circular cross-section, and placed one metre apart in vacuum, would produce between these conductors a force equal to 2×10^{-7} newton per metre of length. [CIPM (1946), Resolution 2, approved by the 9th CGPM (1948)]

Thermodynamic Temperature

The *kelvin*, unit of thermodynamic temperature, is the fraction 1/273.16 of the thermodynamic temperature of the triple point of water. [13th CGPM (1967), Resolution 4]

Luminous Intensity

The *candela* is the luminous intensity, in the perpendicular direction, of a surface of 1/600 000 square metre of a black body at the temperature of freezing platinum under a pressure of 101 325 newtons per square metre. [13th CGPM (1967), Resolution 5]

Amount of Substance

The mole is the amount of substance of a system which contains as many elementary units as there are carbon atoms in 0.012 kilogramme of carbon-12. The elementary unit must be specified and may be an atom, a molecule, an ion, an electron, a photon, etc., or a specified group of such entities.

Appendix III

DICTIONARY OF SI AND OTHER ACCEPTED UNITS

Unit	Abbreviation for unit	SI value	Comment
angstrom Unit	$\overset{\circ}{A}$	10^{-10} m	0.1 mm preferred
arc	a	10^2 m^2	
atmosphere (standard)	atm	101.325 kNm^{-2}	1.01325 bar
atmosphere (technical)	at	98.07 kN m^{-2}	non SI unit
bar	bar	10^5 N m^{-2}	
barn	b	10^{-28} m^2	
Calorie (international)	cal	4.1868 J	
calric (15° c)	4.1855 J		
calrie (20° c)		4.1816 J	
carat (metric)		2×10^{-4} kg	
cheval vapeur	CV	735.5 W	metric horse power
Curie	Ci	37×10^9 s^{-1}	nuclear disintegrations/second
dyne	dyne	10^{-5}N	cgs unit of force
electron volt	eV	1.602×10^{-19} J	
erg	erg	10^{-7} J	cgs unit of energy
fermi		10^{-16} m	atomic unit
grade	g	$\pi/200$ rad	in vogue in France
hectare	ha	10^4 m^2	
hertz	Hz	1 cycle s^{-1}	same as cycle/second (caps)
joule	J	1 Nm	SI unit of work or energy
kilogram	kg		A fundamental unit in SI
kilogram force	kg f	9.806 65 N	
kilopond	kp	9.806 65 N	
kilowatt-hour	kWh	3.6 MJ	

Unit	Abbreviation for unit	SI value	Comment
Lambda	λ	10^{-9} m^3	1 mm^3
litre	l	10^{-3} m^3	1 dm^3
metre	m		A fundamental unit in SI
micron	μ	10^{-6} m	μm preferred
newton	N	1 kg ms^{-2}	SI unit of force
pascal	Pa	1 N m^{-2}	suggested as SI pressure unit
pieze	pz	10^3 N m^{-2}	
poise	P	10^{-1} N s m^2	cgs viscosity unit
poiseulle	Pl	1 Ns m^{-2}	suggested as SI viscosity unit
quintal	q	100 kg	0.1 of a metric ton (tonne)
rad	rad	10^{-2} J kg^{-1}	unit in atomic physics
rayl		10 Ns m^{-3}	acoustic impedence unit
rontgen	R	2.58×10^{-4} C kg^{-1}	
sthene	sn	10^3 N	force unit in mts system
stoke	st	10^{-4} m^2 s^{-1}	cgs unit of kinematic viscosity
thermic	th	4.1855 MJ	
tonne	t	10^3 kg	
torr		133.322 N m^{-2}	$\frac{1}{760}$ atmos
watt	W		

ELECTRICAL UNITS WITH SPECIAL NAMES

Unit	Abbreviation	SI value	Comment
abampere		10A	
abcoulomb		10C	
abfarad		10^9F	Units of cgs absolute emu system
abhenry		10^{-9}H	
abohm		$10^{-9}\Omega$	
abvolt		10^{-9}V	
ampere	A		Base unit of SI unit
biot	Bi	10A	
coulomb	C	1 As	SI charge
farad	F	1 CV^{-1}	SI capacitance unit
gauss	G	10^{-4}T	
henry	H	1 Wb A^{-1}	SI inductance unit
maxwell	Mx	10^{-8} Wb	
mho		$1\Omega^{-1}$	
oersted	Oe	79.58 A turn/m	
ohm	Ω	1 VA^{-1}	
Siemen		1 Ω^{-1}—IEC	approved unit for conductance

Unit	Abbreviation	SI value	Comment
statampere		333.6×10^{-12}A	
stat conlomb		333.6×10^{-12}C	units of cgs absolute csu
stat farad		1.113×10^{-12}F	
stat henry		898.8×10^{9} H	system
stat ohm		898.8×10^{9} Ω	
stat volt		299.8 V	
tesla	T	Wb m^{-2}	SI unit of flux density
volt	V	WA^{-1}	SI potential unit
weber	Wb	Vs	SI unit of magnetic flux

Appendix IV

THE ELECTROMAGNETIC SPECTRUM

The electromagentic waves range from radio-waves of wavelength as long as 10,000 metres to the gamma rays (emitted from radioactive material) which have a wavelength of the order of 10^{-11} mm. They all travel at the same speed through empty space (3×10^8 m s^{-1}) and obey the same fundamental laws.

Since $v = f\lambda$, where v = velocity (ms^{-1}), f = frequency (H), and λ = wavelength (m), it follows that long waves are of low frequency and short waves are of high frequency. Table 1 below gives the latest classification of radiowaves from 10 kH to over 300 MH.

Table 1

CLASSIFICATION OF RADIOWAVES

Frequency range		Wavelength range (metres)		Classification Frequency	Wavelength
30	k Hz		10,000	Very Low—VLF	Myriametre
30	k Hz-300 k Hz	10,000 —	1,000	Low—LF	kilometret
300	k Hz-3 M Hz	1,000 —	100	Medium—MF	hectometre
3	M Hz-30 M Hz	100 —	10	High—HF	dekametre
30	M Hz-300 M Hz	10 —	1	Very High—VHF	metre
300	M Hz-3000 MHz	1 —	0.1	Ultra High—UHF	decimetre
3000	MHz-30000 MHz	0.1 —	0.01	Super High—SHF	centimetre
30000	MHz-300000 MHz	0.01 —	0.001	Extra High—EHF	millimetre

N.B: Note the frequencies are given RHz and MHz instead of the usual kc/s or Mc/s, because 1 c/s = 1 Hz

Appendix V

EXAMPLES OF UNITS CONTRARY TO SI, WITH THEIR SI EQUIVALENT
IN USE AT PRESENT

Physical quantity	Unit	Equivalent in SI	Physical quantity	Unit	Equivalent in SI
			force	dyne	10^{-5} N
length	angstrom	10^{-10}		poundal	0.138 255 N
	inch	0.025/4 m		pound-force	4.44822 N
	foot	0.304/8 m		kilogram-force	9.806 65 N
	yard	0.914/4 m			
	mile	1.609 34 km	pressure	atmosphere	101.325 kn m^{-2}
	nautical mile	1.853 18 km		torr	133.322 Nm^{-2}
				pound (f) sq. in.	6,894.76 Nm^{-2}
area	square inch	645.16 mm^2			
	square foot	0.092 903 m^2	energy	erg	10^{-7} J
	square yard	0.836 128 m^2		calorie (I.T.)	4.186 8 J
	square mile	2.589 99 km^2		calorie (15)	4.185 5 J
				calorie	4.184 J
volume	cubic inch	$1.638\ 71 \times 10^{-5}$ m^3		(thermo chemical)	
	cubic foot	0.028 316 8 m^3	energy	B.t.u.	1 055.06 J
	Imperial	0.004 546 092 m^3		foot poundal	0.042 140 1 J
				foot pound (f)	1.355 82 J
mass	pound	0.453 592 37 kg			
	slug	14.593 9 kg	power	horse power	745.700 W
density	pound/cubic inch	$2.767\ 99 \times 10^4$ $^-$kgm^3	temperature	degree Rankine	5/9 K
	pound/cubic foot	16.018 5 kgm^{-3}		degree Fahrenheit	$t/°F = 9/5 T/°C + 32.$

Bibliography

1. Rao. V.V.L.: INSA Booklets on SI units No. 4, *New Methods for Teaching Electricity and Magnetism, Electronics and Electrical Engineering in SI units* (*for teachers*), The Indian National Science Academy, New Delhi, 1970.
2. Rao. V.V.L.: INSA Booklets on SI units No. 5, *SI Units, Symbols, Signs and Abbreviations*, The Indian National Science Academy, New Delhi 1, 1970.
3. IS: 3616-1966: *Recommendations of the International System* (*SI*) *Units*, Indian Standards Institution, New Delhi.
4. IS: 3722-1966: *Letter Symbols and Signs used in Electrical Technology*, Indian Standards Institution, New Delhi.
5. IS: SP5-1969: *Guide to SI Units*, Indian Standards Institution, New Delhi.
6. Bradshaw, Eric: *Electrical Units with Special Reference to the MKS System*, Chapman & Hall, London, 1962.
7. McGreevy, T.: *The MKS System of Units* (A guide for Electrical Engineers), Sir Isac Pitman & Sons Ltd., London, 1953.
8. *The Teaching of Electricity* (*with special reference to the use of MKS units*): A report of a subcommittee of the Science Masters' Association, John Murray Ltd., London, 1954.
9. Vaughan, W.C.: *"The Electrical Constants of Free Space"*, *Science News,* 41(1956), pp. 75-86.
10. Varner, V.R.: *The Fourteen Systems of Units,* Vantage Press, New York, 1961.
11. Russel, A.W.: *The MKS approach to Electricity and Magnetism*, University of London Press Ltd., 1966.
12. Sayer, Michael: *Notes and Problems in MKS Physics.*
13. Hayes, A.R.W.: *Revision Physics* (for Sixth Form), Longman's, London, 1962.
14. Noakes, G.R.: *New Intermediate Physics* (4th edition), Macmillan, London, 1967.
15. Noakes, G.R. & B.K. Harris: *Foundations of Physics* (*In SI units*), Macmillan, London, 1969.
16. Young, Leo: *Systems of Units in Electricity and Magnetism, Electronics and Electrical Engineering Texts:* 1, Oliver and Boyd, Edinburgh, 1969.
17. Martin, S.L. & A.K. Connor: *Basic Physics in SI Units,* Vol.2, White Combe & Tombs Ltd., Sydney, 1969.
18. Silsbee, Francis. B.: *Systems of Electrical Units,* National Bureau of Standards Monograph 56, 1962, U.S. Dept. of Commerce, Washington.
19. McGlashan, M.L.: "Units Particularly SI Units", *Physics Education,* Vol. 4, pp. 1-11, 1969.
20. Spurgin, C.B.: "SI Units in School Physics", *Physics Education,* Vol. 4, pp. 12-18, 1969.
21. Margolis, D.S.: "Metrication—An apology for SI Units, Electronics and Power", *The Journal of Institution of Electrical Engineers,* London, Vol. 15 December 1969, p. 413.
22. Anderton, P.: *Changing to Metric System,* NPL, Teddington, U.K. HMSO, London, 1969.
23. Blackman, Deane, R.: *SI Units in Engineering* Macmillan & Co., Melbourne, 1969.
24. BS 3763—1964: *International System* (*SI*) *Units* British Standards Institution.
25. BSPD: 5686—1965: *The Use of SI Units*, British Standards Institution.
26. ISO/R 1000—1969: *Rules for the Use of the International System of Units and Selection of the Decimal Multiples and Sub-multiples of the SI Units*
27. Richards, Sears., Wehr., & Zemansky: *Modern College of Physics,* Addison-Wesley Publishing Company, Inc., World Student Series, 1966.
28. Thorley. W.: *Design of Load Bearing Brickwork in SI and Imperial Units based on CP* 111.
29. *Metrication in the Construction Industry No. 1 Metric in Practice, Background and General Principles, SI Units, Dimensional Coordination,* Ministry of Public Building and Works, HMSO London, 1970.